> an entire art fo[illegible]
> graphic depiction [illegible]
> has seemed to b[illegible]
> the 20th century. Where truly appalling acts of violence became defining moments for global culture.[11]

With the rise of information becoming globally and instantly accessible, it is much easier to see the negative and be bombarded by it all at once. Not only that, but because the internet gives us immediate gratification of the information we are looking for, it compounds the bias we already believe. This makes the work of comparing our thinking to the long-term data accumulated almost impossible as all the noise drowns it out. Add the fact that we just walked through a global pandemic (and everything surrounding it), and it can be easy to take our eyes off of the promise of hope. But even in the reality we lived out in COVID-19 (and everything else compounded around it) hope can be found! *Anthemcreative.ca* created a short video that I believe drove this idea home. Here is the transcript of that video:

> For generations, through devastation, heartache, destruction, and evil, humanity has proven its resilience and power. Our history shows that we are masters of the comeback. Our DNA is woven from grit, ingenuity, creativity, and Love. We are lemonade makers. Hope manufacturers. The ones who always get back up. And get back up. And get back up. We counter every blow with a pivot and haymaker after haymaker.
>
> If we cannot gather in person we will harness the digital world and assemble by the masses. We will reshape connection and redeem distraction. We will pick up the pieces and rebuild from this ruble. And we will do it again.

> And again. Because this current reality is not our identity. This devastation will not be our end. It will be the fuel that drives our better future. The powerful comeback that marks our generation.
>
> The proof is in our history, the stake is in the ground. We will not stay down! We will run into our fear, and give it its name. We will tear down our anxiety, surround it with love and remind ourselves that we... are not alone.
>
> And for generations, they will know us by our love. Because this is our secret. It can not be taken from us. So we will love. And we will Grow. And we will rebuild. And we'll do it again. And again. And again.[12]

Here is the plain truth: As a human race, we have shown time and time again that we rise to the task of facing tragedy head-on and bringing new hope in seemingly hopeless circumstances. I wonder if the issue isn't that there are situations where hope cannot reside but that our view is out of focus. Dr. Trench would assert that "when we realize that we have been looking through cloudy glasses, and we have seen things wrongly—it causes the clouds to clear up, and we discover that it's not the end of the world—it's the beginning of a whole new world!"[13]

Let me be utterly clear. I am not promoting the naive idea of putting our heads into the sand and imagining that tragedies don't exist. There is still death, pain, and hardship in life. The issue arises when we can so quickly lose our focus on supernatural hope and its impact because it is being crowded out by the unending bylines of negativity we see. The sad reality is it is easier and more sensational to focus on hopelessness than hope. Max Rose, a writer for *Vox*, makes this very point:

> I do not think they are the only ones to blame, but I do think that the media is to blame for some part of this. This is because the media does not tell us how the world is changing; it tells us what in the world goes wrong. One reason the media focuses on things that go wrong is that the media focuses on single events, and single events are often bad – look at the news: plane crashes, terrorism attacks, natural disasters, election outcomes that we are not happy with. Positive developments, on the other hand, often happen very slowly and never make the headlines in the event-obsessed media.[14]

Hopelessness can be sudden and tragic, while hope is patient, gradual, and sometimes slow. In a world that gets immediate gratification in so many areas of our life, we can often be impatient to see the immediate change (and are drowning in stories of hopelessness) and so, it seems impossible that hope could ever emerge. Or worse, we become dull to the idea that hope could ever be possible.

When bombarded with a reality of hopelessness, it can be easy to become skeptical, cynical, and pessimistic, which perpetuates a movement of discouragement and speaking death into the world. In a world full of pessimism and hopelessness, we desperately need people who bring optimism and hope. In a world where discouragement is the norm and the critics become the loudest voice, we desperately need the encouragers to stand up in that void. Once we admit that our view of the world may be negatively warped, we can be in a position to change the script.

I was wrestling with this very idea when I posed this idea online: "If the encouragers could have the courage to be as tenacious as the critics, the world would be a better place." I hoped that this simple statement would stir some thought, but something else interesting hit me. As people started interacting with it, I would come back and see the words I wrote, again and again. I kept looking at the words 'encourager' and 'courage' and thought, "Wait! The word "encourager" or "encourage" has the word "courage" in it." Was it a coincidence, or was there something to this? So I looked up the definition of the word encourage, and here is what I found:

> The word encourage comes from the Old French word encoragier, meaning "make strong, hearten." When you encourage the tomato plants in your garden, you water them to promote their growth and health. Encourage can also mean to inspire with hope, like when you encourage your friends to try out for the school play by complimenting their singing and acting talents.[15]

The word "encourage", *literally*, and *literarily* has the root word 'courage' in it. To give strength, to hearten, and to give hope to something or someone. Think about this: It takes courage to be an encourager. It takes courage because, in a world where the loudest voices are, more often than not, the cynics, the critics, the naysayers, the argumentative, being anything contrary might just put a target on your own back.

Much like a medic on the battlefield, to be encouraging means to stand in the crossfire of hate, judgment, cynicism, and criticism (though I wonder if the critics don't even realize they are doing it). It means we stand up for the little guy. It means we are willing to mend the broken and bruised while on that battlefield. It means that we also risk the danger of being a target ourselves, and though we wear the red cross of healing and hope, that won't necessarily stop those who wish to take us out.

I have been fortunate to have many people in my life that have played this role. My parents, my siblings, friends, mentors, pastors, bosses, and coworkers (to name a few). But one moment stands out to me as I write this. Throughout our marriage, my wife has been my strongest ally and encourager. She has been one of my greatest supporters through thick and thin and someone who deposits life into me. She doesn't solely do this when I am being pleasant but also when I'm being difficult. She also doesn't merely encourage me with areas of strength but areas of needed growth. She will lift me up when I am struggling but is also someone who calls me to a higher standard when I am willing to settle.

One of those instances came when we were attending a conference together. The speaker challenged us to see there was greater freedom to be had, and we often limit ourselves to the hope we can have in our lives. As they spoke these words, a particular addiction I had struggled with for years came to mind. I remember leaning over to my wife and saying that the battle I was facing would probably be something I would always carry. I said this because, in a sort of way, I believed this was simply part of my story and would be my reality for my life. It wasn't something that had control over me but something I walked with daily. In so many ways, I was a high-functioning addict. The addiction was real and always present but not something that consumed me or controlled my daily actions. But being able to find another level of freedom was not something that I assumed I would experience on this side of the grave. I mean, it had been a part of my story for so long.

What came out of my wife's mouth next stopped me in my tracks. She looked at me and said, "Bull Sh$@#!" To this day, my wife denies she said these exact words. But I remember the instant like it was yesterday because it was a turning point for me. This sort of language is not something you would ever hear my wife say, yet it was precisely what I needed to hear. After the session, we went for a walk and discussed the whole thing.

I had been living in half-measures believing that deeper freedom was out of reach. I mean, I was living a purposeful life with so much to be thankful for; to think there was even more never occurred to me. Even though I battled an addiction, God had been so good and faithful to me, even in this. But this moment became a catalyst that started a journey that allowed me to find freedom in a way I had never experienced before, which spilled into so many other areas of my life since. (we will unpack more of this in chapter 7).

If my wife didn't have the courage to call me out, call me to something greater, and be willing to stand against the things holding me back from experiencing deeper freedom, I might still be captive to false ideas keeping me from what God truly wanted for me. Not only did this moment become the catalyst toward supernatural healing, but I found deeper intimacy with God and others and even saw life-changing healing and reconciliation in my entire family. And it all started because my wife was willing to be courageous to speak the truth into my life. That is the power of the encourager. Their weapons are not of this world and can destroy the strongholds that keep so many imprisoned when wielded right.

Can I be so bold as to call something out? Where are all the encouragers? We need you! Rise up and speak up! The healers, the hope carriers, the world changers. It won't be easy; it takes courage to be an encourager, but even though it is hard, the alternative is unthinkable. If you are an encourager, let me urge you to have the courage to be as tenacious as the critics because it is you that can offset the onslaught of death and hopelessness. It is you who can make the difference between life and death in a single person's world and could cause a spark towards viral change.

What better place to find this wisdom than from Mr. Rogers himself, "If you could only sense how important you are to the lives of those you meet; how important you can be to the people you may never even dream of. There is something of yourself that you leave at every meeting with another person."[16]

There is a power in having a hope-filled perspective that is sparked by ideas that give new life through both action and words. "We need a larger vision. All great movements begin in great ideas. There is no progress without a new thought as its embryo." (A.B. Simpson - *A Larger Christian Life*)[17] Where fear, death, and hopelessness prevail, the light of love, life, and hope can pierce through. It is the very power that mends broken relationships, brings hope to the hopeless, finds cures to diseases, and sees possibilities where others see despair. "A victorious view will inspire you to plan for the future, move ahead with courage, invest in the next generation, and believe God for greater things yet to come. Satan is not taking over

THE REMNANTS OF YESTERDAY

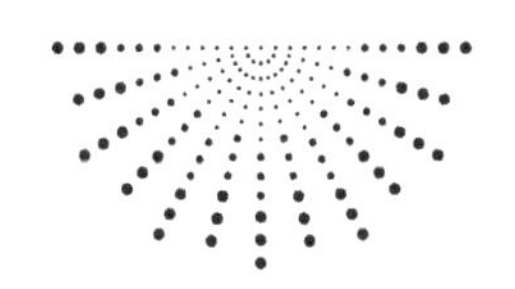

ANTHONY M. STRONG

WEST STREET
PUBLISHING

For Tiki and Gidget
Miss you guys!

CHAPTER ONE

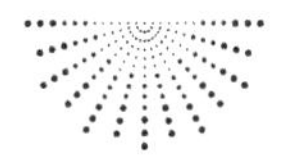

THE WORLD ENDED on a mild Tuesday night in June. There was no fanfare, no warning of what was to come. In the days, hours, and minutes before everything went to hell, people hurried about their business with the certainty that they were safe within their small corners of existence, that the mundane tasks they performed every day would continue on an endless cycle. Waking each morning, brushing their teeth, dropping the kids off at school, going to work, driving home, climbing into their comfortable beds at night.

Rinse and repeat.

They thought they had things all figured out. That life would be like that forever.

I was no different. After all, it wasn't like I had a crystal ball. Besides, even if I had known what was about to happen, I might have driven to that lonely gas station off I-89, anyway. Maybe…

"Can I help you?" The girl behind the counter looked up when I entered the store, alerted by a small bell suspended above the door. Her dusty blue eyes sparkled despite the cold white light given off by the neon tubes set into the false ceiling.

"I need a fill up," I replied. She was cute—much too attractive to be working on her own at night in a gas station off the highway. My eyes fell to the name-tag fixed, slightly askew, above her left breast. Clara. "Thirty dollars on four."

"I think we can arrange that." She flicked a strand of long brunette hair away from her face. "Cash or credit?"

"Credit." I flipped my wallet open and picked a card, the one with the lowest balance, and pushed it across the counter.

She plucked it up and examined it for a moment. "Cool name." Her eyes skipped from the card back to me. "Hayden Stone. Sounds like a rock star or something."

"Yeah, right." Too bad it took more than a cool name to become a rock star. I tried playing guitar for a while in high school. I sucked. Ten years on, I still had no inclination to give it another go.

"Still a cool name."

"Thanks." I glanced through the large window fronting the store, toward my car. "I tried to pay at the pump. The card reader isn't working."

"Yeah. Sounds about right. I'll tell Walter. Not that he'll fix it. If people pay outside they don't come in here and buy stuff."

"Who's Walter?"

"My boss."

From somewhere behind me, I heard a fresh voice. Rasping. Full of a lifetime's cigarette smoke. "And don't you forget it."

A short, balding man in his mid-fifties appeared from the direction of the restrooms. He wore an ill-fitting short-sleeved shirt with buttons stretched just a little too tight, and tan slacks that were fighting his belly for dominance of his waistline.

"That's Walter." Clara scowled. Her eyes met mine for a moment, and I saw a flicker of disgust.

"I've told you before, Clara, you're to call me Mr. Hancock," he scolded, pushing his way behind the counter with a grunt. As he passed her, he brushed close, even though there was more than enough room, and opened the register to inspect the contents. "You'd do well to remember, Clara, plenty of folks would be happy to have your job."

"Yeah, right," Clara said. She swiped my card and waited for the transaction to process. "They'll be lining up around the block."

"One more quip like that and I'll dock your wages," Walter said, turning his attention to me. "Sorry about the sass. Good help is like good whiskey. Hard to find, and there's never enough if it."

"No worries." I caught Clara's eye and smiled.

"Where you heading, son?" Walter asked.

"New York. My brother Jeff. He's having a baby." Actually, it was a double celebration, but I didn't mention the deal I'd just signed for my book. A novel I'd spent the last two years writing, and would finally let me quit my day job. It was none of Walter's business.

"Really? New York?" He scratched his head, the motion dislodging a few flakes of dandruff. "Where are you coming from?"

"Burlington."

"Burlington, huh? Don't go there too often myself. Too many people. I don't like all those noisy crowds." Walter sniffed and rubbed his nose with the back of his hand. "Not that New York's any better, mind you."

"Each to their own." I directed my attention to Clara, who more than likely wished she were anywhere but in close vicinity to Walter. "Are we done?"

"Just about." She forced a smile and handed me a receipt. "Enjoy New York, Hayden Stone."

"That's the plan." I hated leaving her with Walter. He was a pig. For a moment I entertained the thought of jumping the counter, sweeping her up into my arms, and rescuing her—a shining knight with a Volkswagen. Instead I said, "Hope you find a better job real soon."

"Me too." She grinned.

If Walter heard, he ignored it.

The gas station forecourt was deserted. It was late, and I was in the middle of nowhere, which in Vermont is worse than the middle of nowhere in just about anywhere else. I should have waited until morning and set off then, after a good night's sleep, but after Jeff called and said his wife, Becca, had gone into labor, I didn't want to wait. It wasn't like we had any other family to offer support. So I finished up my shift at the coffee shop, dropped by the apartment, packed a bag, and hit the road.

As I filled the tank, I glanced around. Apart from myself, there was only one other customer, a tall woman in a red dress next to a convertible BMW roadster. She smiled when our eyes met. I would have returned the gesture, but at that moment it happened.

Pain slammed into me.

A crushing agony that started in the deepest depths of my brain and punched outward.

It was like being hit by an invisible eighteen wheeler. I grunted and leaned against the car, white-hot daggers of light swarming in front of my eyes. I was sure that any moment now my head would split open, my skull explode from the immense pressure within.

Fear punched through the pain. What was happening? Was I having a heart attack? Worse? Was there even such a thing as worse than a heart attack?

I stumbled forward, trying to get back to the store and Clara. I never even made it two steps, because at that moment, my legs buckled beneath me.

I toppled forward.

The ground raced up too fast.

My vision withered to a pinprick—a long tunnel with consciousness at one end, and myself at the other. And in the split-second before the tunnel collapsed into darkness, I wondered about the woman in the red dress, and why she wasn't rushing to help.

CHAPTER TWO

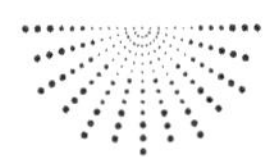

SELF SERVE. GROCERIES. COLD BEER.

A bright white strip of light flickered, blinking like some kind of crazy erratic Morse code, buzzing as it did so.

Where the hell was I? What was I looking at? My addled brain took a second to interpret the strange view, and then it hit me. I was staring up at a canopy. There were words on the side in tall red letters with peeling edges.

I battled to quell a rising panic. I needed to clear my head, make sense of where I was, what I was doing. For a moment my mind remained blank, a void of hazy recollections, disjointed and jarring. Then, just like that, everything snapped back into focus, the memories tumbling over each other. Stopping for gas, my brother in New York, the baby, and the book deal. We were going to party like it was 1999, whatever that meant.

My head hurt. It hurt a lot—I must have cracked it against the ground when I collapsed—but at least I was alive. I was also uncomfortable. The concrete was hard, and there was a stone pushing into the small of my back. I sat up and glanced toward the ground, expecting to see a halo of blood where my head had been. There was none, much to my relief.

I looked around. It was too quiet. Where was the woman in the red dress? What about Clara and Walter? The place was like a ghost town. Surely they must have seen me take a dive, but there were no concerned faces peering down at me, no paramedics checking my vitals. Either I'd only been out for a moment and they hadn't noticed yet, or they didn't give a crap. If it was the latter, that was disturbing.

I pulled myself up, using the car as a crutch, and waited a moment, checking my balance. Whatever had happened, it had passed now. The pain in my head was receding, and my legs were working again.

The BMW still sat at the next pump. The driver's door was open a crack and the hose of a fuel pump snaked from the side of the car like a black rubber umbilical cord. A white Gucci purse rested on the roof of the vehicle, the strap dangling over the side. The woman in the red dress was nowhere in sight. Maybe she had gone to the restroom. That would explain why she hadn't rushed over to help me. But why had she left her purse behind, where anyone could come by and steal it? Didn't women usually take their purse with them when they went to the bathroom? Most of the girls I knew did. Not that it mattered. What did matter was reaching Jeff's place in New York and catching a few winks of sleep before heading to the hospital.

I rummaged in my pockets, looking for my keys.

They should have been there, but they were not. Had I taken them out before pumping gas? If so, they should either be on the roof of the car, a place I had a habit of putting them down, or on the ground, dropped when the pain hit.

After a brief search, two things became obvious. My keys were not on the car roof, nor were they visible on the ground.

Great.

It was hard to go anywhere without my car keys.

I kneeled down, wincing as a jab of lingering pain pulsed

behind my eyes. Reaching under the car, I felt around. After a while, my hand closed over a familiar shape. I gripped the key fob and pulled it out with a grunt of satisfaction. Problem solved.

I rose to my feet and paused, glancing around. Something felt off. The BMW still stood unattended, and not a single vehicle had pulled into the gas station since I had regained consciousness. And I couldn't hear cars on the highway. Maybe that was normal. The interstate was at least a mile away, so it was possible the traffic noise didn't carry this far.

Ignoring the strange feeling that had come upon me, I climbed into the car. My thoughts turned to Jeff, five hours away in New York. The clock on the dash read 10:35 p.m. Had it really been only fifteen minutes since I'd pulled off the highway? It felt like more time had passed. I checked my wristwatch, but it agreed with my dash. Shaking off the weird sense of disconnect, I pushed the car key into the ignition and turned it.

Nothing happened.

Actually, that wasn't strictly true. Something did happen. The engine made a dry clicking sound.

I tried again.

Click.

Albert Einstein once said that insanity is doing the same thing over and over and expecting different results. If that was the case, then I was clearly insane, because I turned the key for a third time, then a fourth. By the fifth attempt, there wasn't even a click.

My battery was dead.

CHAPTER THREE

"HELLO?" I STEPPED inside the convenience store for the second time that evening. The bell above the door jangled. The place was empty. Both Walter and Clara had pulled a vanishing act. Just like the woman in the red dress and the traffic noise on the highway.

A prickle of apprehension wormed up my spine. This was getting too weird.

"Is anyone here?" My eyes wandered over the store, first to the restrooms tucked away in the back corner, then toward the coffee bar, and finally to the service counter. The store was empty. Only the rhythmic hum of an air conditioner broke the eerie silence.

"I could use some help. My car won't start. I think the battery is dead." I called out. "Hello? Clara? Walter?"

Still nothing.

I opened my mouth to call out again, but a sudden thought occurred to me. What if the BMW woman was robbing the place? She could have Clara and Walter tied up and gagged in the storeroom out back. Maybe she was waiting for me to drive off so she could empty the register and get away with no witnesses. My car breaking down would certainly put a crimp in that plan.

I froze, unsure of what to do next.

I could turn and run, but then what? The car was useless, which meant there was no practical means of escape. And what if she had a gun? I wouldn't get ten feet before she took me down. Hell, maybe Walter and Clara were already dead. No, that wouldn't do at all.

My cell phone was in my back pocket, and calling the cops was a better plan. I reached down and pulled it free, pressing the button on top to wake it up.

Nothing happened.

The screen remained dead and dark. Another dead battery. That only left one option: the telephone affixed to the wall behind the service counter. I stepped toward it, leaning over to pull the phone from the cradle.

Then I saw her.

Clara was behind the counter, sprawled on the floor, unmoving. I couldn't tell if she was breathing, but there was no blood, so she wasn't shot. That didn't rule out the possibility that I'd wandered into the middle of a robbery. I glanced around, relieved to find the store still empty, then slipped behind the counter.

"Clara." I whispered her name.

She didn't move.

"Are you okay?"

She still did not respond.

"Dammit." I plucked the phone from the cradle and lifted the receiver. There was a dial tone. Finally, something was going my way.

I punched the keypad. 9-1-1.

There was a burst of static, followed by a monotone voice. "This number is not in service. Please check the number and try again."

What the hell? I punched the number again. This time it rang twice before the same flat voice answered. "This number is not in service. Please check the number and try again."

I set the receiver down on the counter and pondered my situation. Everything started when I collapsed, and since then, things had gotten decidedly weird. Nothing worked, not the car, not my cell phone, not even 911. Clara was still here, thank goodness. She hadn't vanished like everyone else. Although I hadn't yet plucked up the courage to check if she was dead. I slumped against the counter, unsure how to proceed.

I was deciding what to do next when a female voice broke my train of thought.

"Ouch. My head."

I glanced down to find Clara struggling into a sitting position. She rubbed her forehead and looked up at me.

"What happened?" she asked. "Why are you standing over me? What did you do?"

"I didn't do anything," I said hastily, taking a step backwards. "It's not how it looks. I came in here and found you passed out on the floor."

"Still doesn't explain what happened."

"Beats me. I passed out too," I said. "I woke up a few minutes ago. My car won't start."

"Help me up, will you?" She reached out.

I gripped her outstretched hand and pulled her up. "Are you hurt?"

"No." She leaned on the counter, her eyes alighting on the phone. "Were you trying to make a call?"

"The police. I thought the place was being robbed. You looked dead."

"Well, it's not, and I'm not." She winced. "I've had hangovers better than this. Now I wish I hadn't stopped at one glass of wine last night. At least the pain would be worth it."

"It should fade soon. Mine did," I told her. "Do you remember anything that could explain what happened?"

"No. Nothing."

"Are you sure?"

"What kind of question is that? Of course I'm sure. Last thing I remember is you leaving and Walter making some sleazy comment. Then lights out." She pushed past me and opened one of the glass fronted coolers, where she grabbed a bottle of water. "You want one?"

"Sure."

"Here." She tossed me a bottle. "On the house."

"I'm pretty sure Walter would have something to say about that." I twisted the cap off and gulped. The water was ice cold. It felt good on my throat. "Don't you think?"

"Screw Walter. Where is he, anyway?"

"Beats me. You're the only person I've come across since waking up." I drained the last of the water. "He appears to have vanished. Just like the woman in the red dress."

"Huh?"

I pointed through the window toward the BMW. "She pulled in while I was filling up. She's gone too."

"Strange."

"Yeah."

"Maybe Walter abducted her."

"I think that might be a little far-fetched."

"More far-fetched than people vanishing?" Clara grimaced. "It would explain both of them coming up missing. Trust me, Walter's a creep. I can see him pulling a stunt like that. He probably has her in the storage shed out back. Perv."

"And what about us?" I asked. "How did he make us pass out?"

"Good point," she conceded. "I still think he'd do it though, given half a chance."

A thought occurred to me. "Do you have a cell phone?"

"Who doesn't?" She replied. "In my bag. Walter won't let us carry phones on company time."

"Can you get it?"

"Hang on." Clara put her water down and walked toward a door marked PRIVATE. She took a key from her pocket, unlocked it, and stepped inside. Alone again, I suddenly felt vulnerable. She returned moments later, clutching a small brown shoulder purse.

"Take it out."

"Alright, mister impatient. Give me a chance." She dumped the purse onto the counter and unzipped it, rummaging inside before bringing out a silver iPhone. "What now?"

"Turn it on," I said. "Call someone."

"Okay." She pressed the button to wake the phone up. Her brow furrowed. "Odd. It had a full charge when I left home. There's no way it should have gone dead this quick."

"Give it to me." I practically snatched the device from her hand and turned it over, examining it. There was no doubt. Just like my phone and the car battery, it was dead.

"We could plug it in," Clara suggested. "See if it charges."

"Did you bring one with you?"

"No. But we don't need it." She took off again, stopping at a rack near the rear of the store. She searched for a moment, then grabbed a package before rushing back to the counter. She held her prize up. "Replacement charger. All gas stations carry these things."

"You're a genius." I would have kissed her, except she might have taken it the wrong way. "Do the honors?"

"Absolutely." She reached behind the counter and picked up a pair of scissors, slicing into the shrink wrap and freeing the charger, then plugged it in and pushed the connector into the bottom of the phone. "It'll take a few minutes before we can turn it on."

We waited, watching the screen in silent anticipation.

Several seconds passed, then a few more. All at once, the screen lit up.

"It's working," Clara said.

The screen changed from a battery symbol to a picture of Clara with her arms circling a large dog, a Golden Retriever.

"Nice dog. Yours?"

"My parents."

"Oh." I was about to make a comment about my childhood dog, but then realized there were more important things than idle chatter. "Make a call."

"Who?"

"I don't know. Does it matter?"

"How about my roommate, Shelly?"

"Fine." I didn't really care who she called. I wanted to see if she could get through to someone.

She pulled up the address book, selected a number, and hit dial. "I'll put it on speaker."

"Good idea."

She placed the phone back on the counter.

We waited for the call to connect.

After a few seconds of silence, the phone emitted a shrill beep before the home screen came back up.

The call hadn't connected.

"Shall I try again?" Clara reached toward the phone.

"Don't bother." My eyes strayed to the top of the screen and the space where the service bars should have been. Two words jumped out at me.

No Service.

CHAPTER FOUR

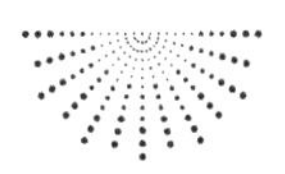

"WHAT NOW?" Clara pulled on her bottom lip with her teeth.

"I don't know."

"None of this makes sense." For a moment she looked like she was about to cry, but she pulled herself together. "We haven't tried my car. Maybe it will start."

"How much do you want to bet?"

"Not much." She narrowed her eyes. "No one else has pulled in since we woke up."

This had occurred to me, too. "Someone should have stopped for gas by now, with the interstate being right down the road."

"It's never this quiet," Clara said. "If people were driving and blacked out like we did..."

"Then the highway is going to be a mess."

"No sirens yet," Clara said. "So maybe not."

"Or maybe there's no one left to respond," I replied grimly. "We could hike to the highway. We might find other people there. People like us."

"Are you kidding me? It's over a mile away, and there are no streetlamps on this road. It'll be pitch black. Besides, I don't want to go outside right now. We're better off staying here. Someone will come eventually. A cop or at least another motorist."

I wasn't so sure about that, but I didn't voice my concern. "We'll stay and wait, then."

"Good." Clara looked relieved. "I'm getting hungry. You want something to eat?"

I looked around the store. "Sure. Do you have anything other than chips and candy?"

"There are some prepackaged sandwiches in the cooler on the back wall. There are some donuts left too."

"A sandwich is fine." I'd planned to stop for food further down the road. "Ham and cheese if you have it."

"I think we can manage that," she said, making her way to the back of the store and opening one of the large coolers. Moments later, she returned with two prepackaged of sandwiches and individual-sized tubs of ice cream. She handed one sandwich to me and kept the other one, then offered me a carton of ice cream. "I found dessert, too."

"Thanks." I took the ice cream.

"Great. Let's eat." She hopped up onto the counter and pulled the wrapper off the sandwich. "Why don't you sit down?" She patted the counter top, inviting me to join her.

"I think I'll stand."

"Suit yourself." She bit into her sandwich, chewing for a moment before speaking again. "So what do you think is going on?"

"I don't know." My mind turned to Jeff in New York. I hoped that whatever was happening here was not also occurring there and that he was safe.

"Maybe it's terrorists." She finished her sandwich and popped the top from the ice cream carton, digging in with a plastic spoon.

"I don't think so." Everyone always thought of terrorism first whenever anything bad happened. I guess it was a sign of the times. "How could terrorists drain our batteries?"

"It could be an EMP."

"A what?"

"Electro magnetic pulse. It fries circuitry so that things stop working. Nuclear explosions can do that." Her bottom lip trembled. "You don't think it was a nuclear strike, do you?"

"We shouldn't jump to conclusions." If it was a missile, New York would be an obvious target, and we were almost five hours away. Would an EMP travel that far? I pushed the thought from my mind, ignoring the knot of dread that roiled in the pit of my stomach. "There was no explosion, no mushroom cloud. We would have heard it. Seen a flash of light when the bomb went off. Besides, your phone came back on."

"I don't follow."

"If something damaged the circuitry, it wouldn't have turned back on. It was only a dead battery."

"Maybe." Clara didn't look convinced.

"Besides, a bomb wouldn't make us pass out."

"Or make people disappear." Clara perked up a bit, but then her face fell. "So we're back to square one. We still don't know what is going on, and we can't contact anyone or get out of here."

"Maybe we can." A thought occurred to me. "If the cell battery just needed charging..."

"Then maybe the car battery is the same." She finished my sentence, a look of hope crossing her face. "That means we can leave."

"Right." There was only one problem. "Do you have a car charger?"

"Again. Gas station." She hopped off the counter and searched the shelves.

"Find anything?"

"Bingo." She held up a set of jumper cables. "How about these?"

"No good." My heart sank. "We don't have another car to use as a jump. We need a trickle charger we can plug into a wall socket."

"Sorry. We don't sell those. Just jumper cables."

"Damn." This was getting frustrating. For a moment I'd harbored hope of getting out of here. "I'm fresh out of ideas."

"I might have one in the trunk of my car."

"What?" Why had she not mentioned this earlier? "Really?"

"My dad put a bunch of crap in there before I left for college. He said it was an emergency pack. There's a gas can, flashlight, and I think he put a charger in too."

"If that's true, I could kiss your father."

"I don't think he'd like that very much." Clara smiled for the first time since everything went to hell. "I parked my car out back. I can go get it now."

"So, what are you waiting for? Go get it."

"Ok." She rummaged in her purse and came out with a set of car keys. "Back in a moment."

Then she was gone.

CHAPTER FIVE

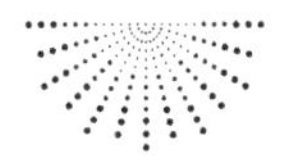

Ten minutes passed. Clara had not returned. I glanced toward the rear door through which she'd left, expecting it to open.

As the seconds ticked away, I wondered if I should have gone with her. After all, we still didn't know what was going on. She should be back by now. Deciding to find her, I took a step toward the door.

The scream was sudden. Shrill.

I jolted, then took off at a run, slamming through the door and stumbling out into the cool night.

It was dark behind the gas station, except for a dim pool of yellow light coming from a rusted security lamp mounted on the gas station's back wall. I looked around, frantic. There was a car parked next to the back fence, near a row of dumpsters. The trunk was open, but there was no sign of Clara.

I rushed toward the car, afraid I might find Clara laying there, really dead this time. I scolded myself for not accompanying her outside. Whatever was I thinking? I rounded the car and scanned the space between the car and the fence, but it was empty.

A second scream carried on the breeze.

It came from a narrow alley on the side of the building.

I turned and raced toward the sound, entering the alley in time to see Clara being dragged backward into the gloom by a dark shape. She struggled and kicked, but she could not break free.

"Hey!" I shouted. "Stop."

The shape paused and turned. I recognized the face in an instant.

Walter.

"Leave her alone." I charged forward, lowering my shoulder as I drew close. I stepped around Clara and shot an arm out, clipping Walter under the chin. His head snapped back. He made a bleating sound and let go of Clara.

"Come on." I reached out and grabbed her arm, steering her away from Walter.

He observed us with angry eyes, mouth opening and closing as if he were trying to speak, but only low grunts came out. He jerked his head from side to side and brought his hands up, slapping his own face. His fingers moved to his scalp, curling into his thinning hair and tugging at it.

I kept backing up, keeping myself between Clara and her suddenly deranged boss. Then, just when I thought we might escape, Walter hunkered down and charged.

"Run!" I pushed Clara back toward the rear of the convenience store and followed, all too aware of the maniac bearing down upon us. We reached the end of the alley. Clara turned the corner and made a dash for the rear door of the store. I was about to do the same, but at that moment, Walter caught up.

He slammed into my back, sending me staggering forward as his arms snaked around my waist. I twisted, attempting to pry myself free. But he was deceptively strong. Finally, as a last resort, I brought my arm back, ramming an elbow into his face. His nose splintered. Hot blood sprayed my neck. He let out a high-pitched squeal and slackened his grip long enough for me to pull away and turn to face him.

Walter was a mess. Blood seeped from his ruined nose. It trickled down his chin and onto his shirt. A mix of spittle and some kind of brown mush that looked like dirt fell from his mouth as he spewed a tirade of guttural sounds that bore little resemblance to speech. Judging from the brown stains on his hands, I concluded he had, at some point prior to attacking Clara, actually been eating dirt.

I scanned the area for anything to use as a weapon. My eyes alighted on a stack of propane tanks near the dumpsters along the back fence. Not perfect, but they would do.

"What are you doing?" Clara lingered next to the door. "Get inside."

"Give me a moment." Walter was eyeing me the way a person might look at a fat, juicy steak.

"Don't be stupid." Clara was frantic.

"Hang on." I backed up, edging toward the tanks.

Walter watched me for a moment, seemingly oblivious to the blood that was still flowing from his nose, and then he took a step forward.

I could guess what was about to happen, and Walter did not disappoint. I ducked sideways as he leaped forward. The tanks were not far away. I reached them and snatched one up. They were empty, just as I suspected. If they had been full, there was no way I would have been able to hoist one, thus ruining my plan.

Walter closed the distance between us with astonishing speed, considering his girth and age. He lowered his head, intent upon ramming me. When he was less than two feet away, I swung the canister upward as hard and high as I could.

Walter ran right into it.

My aim was not great. As a means of self-defense, a propane tank is not the most graceful of instruments. Luckily, my assailant was too mad or too stupid to duck. The canister clipped him, a glancing blow under the chin with a hollow thud. Walter's head snapped to the side. He performed a perfect pirouette, and then his legs gave way. The jarring off kilter impact sent a stab of pain up my arm, and I lost grip on the tank. It fell to the ground and rolled away, finally coming to rest against the closest dumpster.

Walter was down.

I waited a moment, expecting him to spring back up unharmed like some monster in a slasher movie. But thankfully, he didn't move.

"Is he dead?" Clara rushed forward, stopping short of Walter. "Did you kill him?"

"No." I said. "He's still breathing."

"Shame." Clara edged closer, warily eyeing her prone boss. A tear rolled down her cheek. "He was going to kill me. Or worse."

"You're safe now."

"He came out of nowhere. I wasn't paying attention." She wiped the tear away. "Stupid."

"Not at all." I looked down at Walter. He was still unconscious. "Did you find a charger?"

"Yes." She glanced toward the car.

"Good. Maybe we can get out of here by morning."

"I don't want to wait that long." Clara looked dismayed. "Can't we leave now?"

"It'll take several hours to charge the battery."

"Just great." She looked down. "So what do we do with Walter?"

"We tie him up, and then we lock ourselves inside until dawn."

CHAPTER SIX

"THAT SHOULD DO IT." I pulled on the nylon rope, making sure there was no give. Walter was still out cold, but he wouldn't stay that way forever, and I didn't want to take any chances.

"Will that hold him?" Clara asked.

"Four years in Boy Scouts says it should." I had spent the last ten minutes heaving Walter from the back of the gas station to the front, dragging his dead weight with my arms looped under his. I propped him in a sitting position against the closest pump and wiped my brow, then wrapped several loops of cord around his torso and tied it off. Clara followed behind, brandishing a crowbar from her car's trunk lest Walter awake from his slumber and have another go at us.

"The Boy Scouts?" Clara asked. "That's what we're relying on here?"

"Hey, don't knock the Scouts. They taught me many useful things. Besides, we'll monitor him, just to be on the safe side." I had deliberately chosen the nearest pump so that we could see our prisoner through the window. I would have preferred not to be in such proximity, but I also felt safer knowing where he was.

"I don't like it out here." Clara eyed the darkness beyond the gas station forecourt.

"We need to hook up the battery charger, then we can go back inside." I shared her concern. There could be other people out there—more crazies like Walter—affected by whatever cataclysm had befallen us, and I had no desire to meet them.

"Hurry. Please?"

"Keep a lookout." While I was working on Walter, Clara had found an extension cable in the stockroom. She plugged it in to an exterior socket and ran the cord across the forecourt to my car.

"Will this take long?" She was holding the crowbar so tight her knuckles turned white.

"Nope." It only took a second to plug the charger in and connect the crocodile clips. I checked my work, then brushed my hands on my jeans. "All done."

"Good. Now can we go back inside?"

"You read my mind." I straightened up, my eyes wandering down the road as I did so, toward the highway. A faint red glow pulsed on the horizon. I pointed toward it. "Look at that."

"I noticed it while you were tying Walter up," she said. "What do you think it is?"

"Fire." I'd seen that same glow a few years earlier while on vacation hiking along the Solstice Canyon Trail near Los Angeles with friends. The forest fires had been bad that year, and although we weren't close, we could still see them. "Something's burning on the interstate."

Clara shot me a fearful glance. I knew what she was thinking. Then she shook her head and turned from the glowing horizon. "We're not safe here. Let's go back inside."

CHAPTER SEVEN

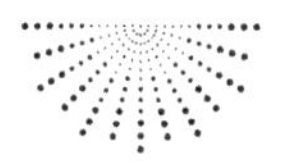

As soon as we stepped into the store, I locked the doors. "We'll need to secure the back door, too."

"Already took care of that when I got the extension cable. No one's getting in the back."

"Good. Are there any other ways inside? Other doors or windows?"

"Not as far as I know. There are windows in the restrooms, but I don't think they open, and they're too small and high to get through easily, anyway." She thought for a moment. "That's it, I think."

"Then we're safe here until the car's battery charges," I said. "Sure would be nice if we could get a message to the outside world, though."

Clara picked up her phone and examined it. "Still no service."

"I didn't expect there to be." Regardless, I was disappointed. "You should rest."

"How can I do that after what's happened?"

"You have to try. We'll need to be alert tomorrow. I don't know what we'll find out there, but if Walter is anything to go by, it will not be good." Once again, my thoughts strayed to Jeff. Was he safe? Was he even still alive? What about his wife and the baby? If this happened in New York while she was in labor… it didn't bear thinking about. God, I hoped they were ok.

"What about you?"

"I'm going to stay awake and watch our friend." I nodded toward Walter. "We'll switch later."

"Well, alright." She didn't sound convinced. "But I doubt I'll sleep."

"Just do your best." I slipped my jacket off and handed it to her. "Here. Use this as a pillow. It's not much, but…"

"Thanks." She took it and sat down with her back against the service counter, then propped the coat behind her head before looking up. "Promise you won't go out there?"

"What, are you crazy? One wrestling match with your boss was enough for me." I could tell she was shaken up, so I added, "I'll be over near the door. I'm not going anywhere. I won't step outside. Promise."

"Okay." She smiled and closed her eyes.

I watched her for a moment, then made my way to the display rack nearest the door and settled on the floor facing the forecourt. And the newly minted madman, Walter.

CHAPTER EIGHT

"WAKE UP!" Someone was shaking me.

I didn't want to wake up. I knew I was dreaming, but the dream was too comfortable. I was in New York with Jeff and his wife. They were cradling a baby. We were laughing and joking, my brother ribbing me about my height—he was a whole inch taller than me—and sharing stories of my lack of athletic prowess back in high school. It was just like always when we were together, and everything was fine with the world.

"Come on, wake up." The shaking was getting more insistent now. "He's gone."

"What?" I snapped awake, the dream fading until it was nothing more than a vague recollection. I must have dozed off. Not a good way to impress Clara with my macho skills. "What's going on?"

"Walter." She waved a hand toward the gas pumps. "He's not there anymore."

I blinked the sleep from my eyes and looked through the window. It was light out, the long rays of the early morning sun casting a golden hue over the forecourt. Walter was nowhere in sight. "Dammit."

"How long were you sleeping?" Clara asked.

"Not sure," I said. It could have been thirty minutes or two hours.

"So what do we do now?"

"Exactly what we planned to do. We get in the car and drive the hell out of here."

"With that maniac on the loose?" She said, her eyes narrowing to angry slits. "Not a chance."

"We don't have a choice," I replied, doing my best to keep my voice level and calm. "It's been eight hours, and in all that time not one person has stopped for gas. We haven't seen a single car drive past, and there's no sign of the emergency services. No cops or firefighters. Nothing. Our phones don't even work."

"We should have gone last night. While we had Walter tied up."

"What with? The car battery was dead." I threw my arms in the air. "Did you try your car when you went to get the charger?"

"It didn't start." She was calming down now.

"Besides, even if I had seen Walter escaping, what would you have me do, go out there on my own and subdue him all over again?" I felt vindicated by this logic. "It took a propane tank upside the head to bring him down last time, remember?"

"An empty propane tank." She tried to suppress a smile. It didn't work.

"Still counts," I replied, happy the situation had diffused itself. "He's probably long gone by now, anyway. I vote we gather up our stuff, pack some snacks for the road, and get the hell out of here."

"Fine. But I'm not leaving without this." She picked up the crowbar. "Now I'm ready to go."

CHAPTER NINE

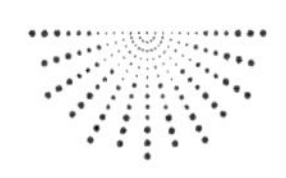

"Keep your eyes open for Walter," I said as we stepped from the safety of the convenience store out onto the gas station forecourt. "Or anyone else who looks like they may have joined the ranks of the crazies."

"No shit." Clara brandished the crowbar like she was carrying a machine gun. Her eyes darted from side to side.

We moved forward slowly, making our way past the abandoned BMW toward my car. As we passed the pump where we tied Walter only a few hours before, my eyes fell on the nylon rope.

Clara saw it, too. She reached down and plucked it from the concrete. Two frayed ends hung loose in her hand, even though the knot was still tied. There were rows of linear indentations in the weave around the ragged ends. She inspected them with narrowed eyes. "These look like—"

"Teeth marks." I finished her thought.

"Oh, my God. He chewed his way free." Clara's eyes were wide with shock. "How is that possible?"

"He obviously didn't appreciate being tied up." The thought of biting through a nylon rope made my teeth hurt.

"It must have taken a while to do this."

"I don't want to think about it." Clara dropped the rope and focused her attention on the car. "We should leave before anything else happens."

"You won't get any argument from me." We hurried toward the car, aware that we might cross paths with Walter again at any moment. "Hop in while I disconnect the charger."

"Keys?"

I threw them to her, then sprinted around the front of the car, leaned into the engine compartment, and unclipped the charger cables. The positive terminal sparked with a gratifying pop of electricity when I pulled the clip off. "Okay, start her up."

There was a moment of silence, then the engine turned over. It caught for a moment, but then fell off to a grinding cough.

"Try again." I poked my head around the hood.

"Okay." Clara turned the key a second time, and again it resulted in nothing but a rasping, choked rattle.

"Dammit."

"The check engine light just came on," Clara said. "Plus a bunch of other lights. It looks like Christmas on the dash."

"Try it one more time." The knot of frustration in my stomach told me it was no good, but I didn't want to give up yet.

"Here goes."

Same again. The engine shuddered and sputtered, but did not roar to life.

"That's enough. It's pointless." A blinding anger welled up inside of me. I grabbed the charger and lofted it with all my might. It bounced off a pump and crashed to the ground several feet away, unharmed. I leaned on the front of the car and stared, forlorn, at the engine, as if I might have an epiphany and figure out what was wrong. No such bolt of mechanical inspiration struck me.

After a minute of silence, Clara spoke up. "Now what?"

I slammed the hood down and looked at her through the windshield. "Now we walk."

CHAPTER TEN

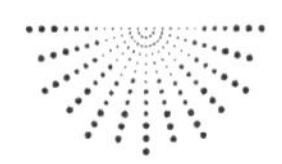

We didn't pass a single vehicle on the way to the interstate. The two-lane road was empty. We walked in silence, both of us consumed by our own worries. We sported backpacks liberated from the convenience store on our shoulders, which we filled with as much food and bottled water as we could carry. I had also transferred most of the clothing from my overnight bag. I would have taken the bag itself, but it was cumbersome, and would have weighed me down. We hiked along the interstate to Clara's college, since it was only one exit down. Then we'd make further plans, depending upon what we discovered there. She could use a change of clothes anyway, and I could tell she was worried about her roommate.

It wasn't until the highway was in sight that we got our first glimpse of the devastation the previous evening's event had caused.

"Look." Clara spotted the car first. It was sitting half off the road, nose down in a ditch, with its rear wheels a foot in the air.

"They must have been coming off the ramp and lost control."

"Do you think they blacked out like us?"

"Don't know." We drew close to the car. I scanned the ground. "There are no skid marks, no rubber on the road."

"What does that mean?"

"It means they didn't slam on the brakes." I peered in the window. The airbags had deployed, but there was no sign of anyone inside. "It's empty."

"Then that means they got out okay. Right?" Clara was eyeing the front of the car, which had crumpled upward when it hit the ditch. One wheel was bent out at a crazy angle, the tire flat.

I reached down and pulled on the door handle, then went to the other side and did the same. "They're locked."

"What?" Clara tried a handle, too. "That's impossible. How did the driver get out?"

"This just keeps getting weirder, doesn't it?" I turned from the car. "Come on."

"Where?"

"Up there." I pointed to the off ramp.

"I'm not sure I want to know what's up there." Clara looked nervous.

"I don't think we have much choice." I wished I could tell her everything would be fine, but I had a feeling we would not like what we saw on the Interstate. "Besides, there might be people up there."

"I suppose." Clara did not look convinced, but followed me anyway as I made my way to the ramp and started up, looking back every once in a while to make sure she was still with me. As the ramp leveled out and joined the Interstate, we saw for the first time the cause of the glow we'd seen on the horizon the previous evening.

I stopped, shocked.

Clara, who was only a few feet behind me, almost walked into me, her attention fixed on the scene of carnage that now presented itself.

"What the hell..." she spoke in a whisper, her eyes wide.

A pall of acrid black smoke hung over the highway, under which sat the remains of several cars, some burned out, others shunted into each other, a couple upturned, their wheels pointing skyward as if they were accusing some angry god of smiting them. Here and there, flames still licked at a few smoldering wrecks. Further down the highway a thick column of smoke weaved into the sky, rising for hundreds of feet before being carried eastward on the wind. One vehicle, closer than the others, sat crumpled against the safety barrier, its right side torn away, the interior scorched almost beyond recognition. The remains of the driver looked at us through empty eye sockets surrounded by black, charred flesh. His hands, if indeed it had been a man, still gripped what remained of the steering wheel even though his arms were nothing more than bone and gristle. The rancid stench of death permeated the air like a sickly perfume.

I heard Clara gag. She turned away and bent over.

"Are you okay?"

"Give me a minute." Her voice sounded hollow.

"We can go back down," I said. There were other wrecks dotting the highway for as far as the eye could see. I was sure this wasn't the worst of what we'd find.

"No." She straightened up and wiped her mouth. "We need to get to the college. This is the quickest way."

"Okay." I reached down and took her hand.

She closed her fingers over mine, and we walked.

CHAPTER ELEVEN

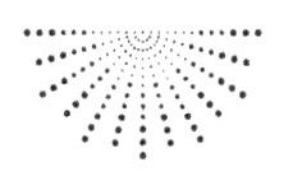

WE HAD BEEN WALKING for about half an hour when we came upon the cause of the rising smoke column. At first I couldn't make out what I was looking at, but as we drew closer, I recognized the familiar shape of a commercial jetliner, or at least the broken remains of it, blocking our path ahead. The terrain was uneven. The highway cut across a steep slope bounded on one side by a steadily ascending wall of rock, and on the other by a steep drop off that reached flatter ground about eighty feet down. The airplane had punched into the side of the hill, leaving the slope strewn with wreckage. The front section, the cockpit and about a quarter of the fuselage, had smashed into the highway and buckled against the cliff, demolishing a large portion of asphalt.

I spotted a wing, its aluminum skin burned and black, then part of the passenger section, open to the sky as if peeled apart by a huge can opener. Next to this, a wheel and landing strut stuck straight up out of the soft ground, almost like it was still doing its job, only there was nothing above it except a mangled mess of wiring and torn metal.

"Oh my God." Clara looked frightened. "It looks like it just fell out of the sky."

"I think that is exactly what happened." The smell of burned jet fuel lingered in the air. If we were unsure that this was an event of greater proportion than our immediate area, the sight of the downed aircraft, and lack of any emergency response, confirmed it.

"Is it safe?" Clara asked. "It's not going to explode or anything?"

"I don't think so." I could see a jet engine laying in a depression near the road. The turbines shattered and burned. "I think it did all of its exploding already."

"This is horrible." She looked like she was about to burst into tears. "Do you think there were many people onboard?"

"It's a big plane." I couldn't tell what type of plane it was, but from the amount of wreckage, and the recognizable logo painted on the vertical stabilizer, it was almost certainly a passenger aircraft.

"What do you think happened to it?" Clara asked.

"Same thing that happened to us. Only we weren't in the air when we blacked out and all the batteries stopped working." The aircraft had not completely disintegrated upon impact, which meant it must have been fairly low when it went down, probably taking off from Burlington Airport. Here and there on the hillside I could see rows of chairs, some with blackened bodies still strapped in. Other seats were empty. "They never stood a chance."

"How are we going to get past?"

"We're not." There was no way around on the right. The rock face was almost vertical. I picked out the remains of old dynamite bore holes. Vertical shafts drilled into the rock by construction workers when they blasted the roadway out of the hillside. The downward slope on the left might have been an option if not for the amount of debris. As it was, we could never negotiate such a steep drop and also climb over the shattered remains of the plane. That left the road and the wrecked cockpit. "We'll have to go through it."

"I'm not climbing through that." There was a look of horror on her face.

"We don't have a choice," I told her. "It's that or we turn back."

"We can't," Clara said. "I need to get to the school."

"Then we go forward." We were almost upon the wreckage now. I could see the deep gouge the impact had made on the roadway. I pushed a piece of twisted metal to the side and picked my way forward, then looked back at Clara. "Be careful. There are a lot of sharp edges."

"We're really going to do this?"

"Yep." The ruined cockpit loomed large over us. I chose my footfalls with care, aware that the ground under my feet was unstable, and approached the wreck. Ahead of me a service hatch hung open below a large hole in the floor of the main cabin. Beyond that was a jumble of debris. I motioned to Clara. "I think we can get through here if we're careful."

"There?" She didn't look convinced. "We're going to climb into the plane?"

"It's the only way." I reached out and gripped the edge of the hatch, testing to make sure it would not give way, then pulled myself into the aircraft.

"What about me?" Clara looked up at me.

I leaned down. "I've got you; hold on to my wrists and climb up."

"Okay." She paused, took a deep breath, and then gripped my hands before finding a foothold on the side of the fuselage and scrambling up. She stumbled forward into the aircraft, swaying for a moment before regaining her balance.

"You good?" I asked her.

"Sure." She brushed a smudge of soot from her arm. "Can we move on? I don't want to linger any longer than necessary."

"Me either." My eyes roamed our surroundings, looking for the best way through. On our right was the cockpit, while on the left the remains of what was business class fell away on a downward slope until it ended in a mess of twisted, torn metal. I counted ten seats. Most were empty, but two were not. A pair of passengers hung limp from their seatbelts. One wore a gray suit, now ripped and dirty, the other a shredded polo shirt. It didn't look like this part of the plane had burned. Maybe it detached upon impact and was spared the almighty fireball that surely ensued as the jet fuel ignited. Despite that, these two had fared no better than the burned up passengers in the rear sections. Their bodies were shredded, pummeled by flying debris and deadly shards of metal.

"Oh, I think I'm going to be sick." Clara was shaking, and her bottom lip trembled. She gripped my shoulder.

"Don't look at them. Turn away."

"I'm not sure that will do any good." Her voice wavered as she spoke. She covered her mouth with one hand, the other still gripping my shoulder like a vice.

"Let's keep moving." I heaved a service cart aside. It teetered for a moment, and then toppled, tumbling down the aisle and out into the emptiness beyond. A few moments later there was a thud as it smacked into the hillside somewhere far below us. "Try to focus your attention ahead."

"I'll try."

"Good." I took her hand, and we carefully worked forward toward a large opening ripped out of the fuselage ahead. The wreckage shifted under our weight. I stopped and waited, praying that it would not slip from the road and tumble down the hillside, carrying us with it.

"We're moving," Clara said, gripping my hand tight.

"It's fine. Keep still for a moment, it will settle down."

"And if it doesn't?"

"Then we run for the opening as quick as we can and hope we make it," I said, doing my best to keep my balance on the shifting debris.

"That doesn't sound like much of a plan," Clara replied. "Got anything else?"

"No." I felt the craft tremble and thought it would go over the edge. But then, mercifully, it settled back down. After a few moments, sensing that the worst was over, I chanced a step forward. The wreckage held. "I think we're fine."

"I hope so." Clara followed me, keeping her eyes down toward the ground.

I stepped over a suitcase, its contents spilled across the floor. To my right was the cockpit. The door lay torn from its hinges. Unable to help myself, I glanced inside, steeling myself against the sight of the traumatized bodies I was sure to find, but the cockpit was empty, the seats strewn with glass from the broken windshield and pieces of the crushed instrument panels.

"Where are the pilots?" Clara voiced what I was thinking.

"No idea. Maybe they got out." But I didn't believe it myself. It was unlikely they would have survived such a devastating impact. There was little time to reflect on it, however. The front section of the plane could lose its battle with gravity and plummet down the hillside at any moment, and I didn't want to be there when it did. "Come on, let's get out of here."

We climbed forward, moving a little faster as we neared the torn hole that served as our escape from the wreck. There should have been a passenger door, but the shell of the plane was stripped away, exposing the interior supports between the outer skin and the passenger sections. All that remained was one twisted hinge. Wiring and the remains of an overhead locker hung down, partially blocking the hole. Below that was a drop of almost six feet.

"We're pretty high up," Clara said, peering over.

"I know."

"What are we going to do?"

"We'll jump." I felt my throat tighten as I said the words. Jumping was the last thing I wanted to do.

"Together?" Clara asked, a look of panic on her face.

"I'll go first," I said. "I think I can make it if I'm careful, then I'll help you."

"Are you sure?" Clara said. "Maybe we should find something to help us climb down."

"We don't have the time," I told her. "This section of the plane isn't safe. With all of our movement in here, it could go at any time."

"If you're sure."

"Sure as I'll ever be." I took a step to the edge of the hole and looked down. The ground below was broken, parts of the asphalt missing entirely. Pieces of the plane, jagged and sharp, were scattered, along with shoes, coats, carry-on bags and even a stuffed bear with one arm missing and white fluffy stuffing poking through the wound.

"Here goes," I said, trying to control the slight quaver in my voice. There wasn't much margin for error. If I didn't land exactly in the right place, I might go over the edge, or worse, impale myself on a piece of wreckage. Finally, realizing it was now or never, I took a deep breath and launched myself out of the airplane.

The ground rushed up fast.

I prepared for the worst, falling down the slope to my death, breaking an ankle, or landing on one of the wicked sharp pieces of debris. Incredibly, none of that happened. Instead, I hit the ground square, my legs buckling under me and absorbing the impact. I dropped to my knees, putting my hands out to break my fall.

"Are you alright?" Clara's voice sounded from above.

I looked up to see her peering out of the hole.

"Yes. I think so." I stood up, wary of any unforeseen injury, but I was fine. I'd made it.

"What about me?" Clara asked.

"You're next. You are going to jump and I will catch you." I planted my feet and reached up, letting her know I was ready. "Come on."

"I can't." She shook her head.

"Yes, you can."

"It's too far. I'm scared."

"Don't be. I won't let anything happen to you," I shouted up to her. "But you have to jump. It's the only way."

"Well–"

"Just do it. Don't think about it," I said, coaxing her. "Do it right now."

"Please make sure you catch me, okay?" She stepped to the edge, a look of determination on her face, and stepped off the side of the airplane.

She dropped toward me fast. Right before she hit the ground, I closed my arms around her and together we tumbled backward. She landed on top of me, her body pressed against mine, and there we lay, not moving for the longest time. Then, when she realized we were both fine, she pushed herself up, dusted herself off and said, "Let's go."

CHAPTER TWELVE

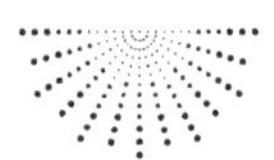

IT TOOK ANOTHER TWO and a half hours to reach the next exit, and by the time we got there, we had witnessed enough death to last a lifetime. We didn't talk about the airplane with the bodies still strapped into their seats. There was enough carnage ahead of us on the highway without thinking about the gruesome sight inside the wrecked plane. Once in a while we came across an empty stretch of road, and that was a welcome respite, but there were always more wrecks up ahead, more broken and burned bodies.

Two hours into our journey, however, I noticed a trend. Some cars and trucks lacked occupants, just like the car at the bottom of the off ramp and the plane's cockpit. A few vehicles stood with their doors ajar, which clearly indicated that the people inside had escaped unharmed, or at least with minimal injury. Others were so totally wrecked it appeared impossible that anyone could have survived. Some, those that hadn't burned, still had seat belts buckled, despite being devoid of their human cargo. Try as I might to figure it out, a rational explanation eluded me, and in the end I gave up trying.

After leaving the interstate behind, we walked for a while,

lost in our own thoughts. Neither of us felt inclined to engage in idle chat after the horrors of the highway. We still encountered the odd car, but these didn't display anywhere near the level of damage, and they were all empty, much to my relief.

Eventually, we reached a small side road and turned up it, finding ourselves at a set of wrought-iron gates flanked by two large brick pillars. An ornate arch spanned the gap between them. White painted lettering followed the curve of the arch.

Ripton College.

"This is it." Clara looked back at me, her face full of hope and worry, then stepped past the gates. "Come on."

We traversed a long driveway flanked by centuries old oak trees that formed a corridor leading to the main campus, which was dominated by a large house that looked like it dated back to the nineteenth century, or even earlier.

The driveway exited the trees and split in two, running off to each side of a large three-tiered fountain, only to swoop back inward in front of the house. To the left and right of the driveway were other buildings, some old, some new. The mix of modern construction and classical architecture should have been strange together, but it worked, each structure offsetting and complimenting the others. Clara made a beeline for the main building, her feet crunching on the gravel driveway as she walked.

"It looks old," I said as we approached the building and climbed the steps to the main entrance. "Really old."

"It is," she said. "The main house dates back to 1855. It was built for a general who later fought in the Civil War. I don't remember which one. It was gifted to the state after the Second World War when the last heir died. That's how Ripton College was founded. It was the first building on campus, and they built the campus up around it."

"Nice." I glanced around. The place was deserted. "Where is everyone?"

"I was wondering the same thing," Clara said, approaching the door. "It's usually really busy at this time of the day."

"Maybe they evacuated the place?" I could think of no other reason why the school would be deserted.

"I don't think so." Clara glanced toward the parking area. "There are still cars here, and besides, how would they do it? The highway is pretty much impassable." She took a swipe card from her pocket and ran it through a reader. A buzzer sounded, and the door clicked open, granting us access.

We stepped across the threshold into a large foyer; the walls covered with portraits in ornate gold frames. An imposing grand staircase of dark polished wood dominated the center of the room. Corridors ran to the left and the right.

Clara paused for a moment, clearly disappointed. Her eyes wandered from the staircase to the corridors, then up to the floor above. "Damn. I thought we might find someone here."

"Sorry." I had hoped there would be some sign of life inside the building, but it was becoming clear that we were on our own. "What now?"

"We go to the dorms; maybe someone will be there."

CHAPTER THIRTEEN

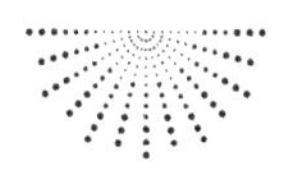

THE INSIDE OF THE BUILDING smelled musty in that odd, dusty way that academic institutions often do. Clara led me past the staircase, down a narrow corridor, and through a back door that opened out onto a central courtyard surrounded by three more buildings. This area too was empty, but Clara did not stop to ponder upon it.

She hurried across the courtyard, making a beeline for the furthest building. When we reached the largest of the buildings, she stopped and pulled the key card out once more.

"These are the dorms." She swiped the key card for a second time, pushed the door open and stepped inside, her face falling when she saw that this space was also abandoned.

"I was hoping..."

"I know." I cut her off. "Where's your room?"

"This way." She moved toward a set of narrow stairs and climbed. When we reached the third floor, she led me down a long corridor and stopped at a plain brown door.

"This is my room." She swiped her card through yet another reader and stepped inside.

I followed her, letting the door close behind us, and then

took stock of my surroundings. The room was small but comfortable, with two beds, one against each wall. Two small closets framed a lead paned window on the far wall. Under the window was a desk cluttered with books of all shapes and sizes.

Clara stood in the middle of the room, a look of disappointment on her face. "She's not here."

"Who?"

"Shelly, my roommate." She turned to me. "I know it seems silly. We haven't seen anyone else on campus, but I was hoping she was here. I wanted her to be safe."

"She might be. Just because she's not here..." I trailed off. A part of me wanted to reassure her, but another part of me, a bigger part, knew that Shelly might be anything but safe. We didn't know where the faculty and student body had gone, and although it was comforting to think they evacuated, rescued by a passing National Guard unit or airlifted out, it didn't seem likely, given all we'd seen so far.

"It doesn't matter." Clara sniffed and wiped away a tear. She took her backpack off and threw it on the nearest bed, then stepped over to the desk and pulled a laptop from the drawer.

"What are you doing?" I asked.

"The internet. We can find out what's going on."

"Of course." I hadn't thought of that. The cell phones might be out of action, but maybe we could still get on the web.

She bent down and plugged in the charger. "I'm sure the battery is dead."

We waited while the machine booted, which took a frustratingly long time. She tapped in a password at the prompt, then opened up the web browser.

She turned to me. "Thank God. We have a wireless signal. What should we try?"

"CNN?"

She typed in the URL.

The browser instantly returned the message: SERVER NOT FOUND.

"Damn." She typed another domain into the browser. The same message popped up. "I don't get it. The computer says it has a wireless signal."

I got it though. "We have a signal from the router. I bet the router doesn't have an outside Internet connection."

"You're right." She looked glum.

"Hey, cheer up," I said. "I didn't even think of it."

"Oh well. It was worth a try." She stood for a few moments looking at the useless laptop, shrugged, and turned back toward me. "You should charge your cell phone."

"What's the point? No service, remember?"

"I don't know. I think we should cover all our bases."

I reached into my pocket and pulled out my phone, then rummaged in my backpack for the charger that we had taken from the gas station. "What now?"

"We should get cleaned up. You look like an axe murderer."

I looked down at myself, at the polo shirt spattered with Walter's blood. I also had dark smudges of soot from the burned-out vehicles on it. "I do, don't I?"

"There are showers down the corridor on the left." Clara pulled a set of fresh clothes from the closet. "We'll be able to think more clearly once we've freshened up."

"You go first." A hot shower sounded good, but I had a feeling Clara needed it more.

"How about we shower together?" she said, grabbing a shower caddy from the nightstand.

"I don't think-"

"Get your mind out of the gutter." She blushed a little. "I'm not seducing you. Separate cubicles. I just don't think we should split up right now."

"Oh. Of course." It was a good idea to stick together, but I also suspected that she didn't want to be alone.

CHAPTER FOURTEEN

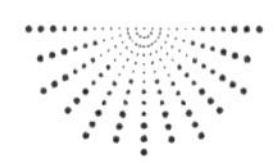

THE SHOWERS WERE ARRANGED along one wall of a large, white tiled room. There were six cubicles, each with a plain cream curtain suspended from a metal rod. Along the other wall was a row of porcelain sinks mounted under large rectangular mirrors.

"You can take the shower closest to the door," Clara said. "That way if we run into any trouble you can protect us." She pulled a couple of towels from a locker near the door and draped one over each stall.

"I'm hoping we won't have that problem." I peeled my top off, dismayed to see that Walter's blood had seeped all the way through and left red blotches on my chest.

"Me either. But just to be safe…" Clara pulled at the buttons of her work shirt and slipped it off, discarding it on the floor. "Won't be needing this anymore."

"What, you don't think Walter will take you back?" I grinned, a feeble attempt at humor.

"I think trying to kill your employee is a sure sign you don't want to work with them anymore."

"I'd say so," I replied, glancing over as she undressed.

She stripped off her khaki pants and dropped them next to the shirt. When she turned oward me, I averted my eyes, but apparently not quickly enough. "That's all you get," she said, and padded toward the second cubicle in her underwear, then pulled the curtain closed. A moment later, I heard the steady drum of water as she turned the shower on.

I followed suit, taking the shower next to her and basking under the hot spray, relishing the way it played over me, soothing and comfortable. "I saw a pile of books on the desk back there. Shakespeare, Capote, and some Hemmingway too, I believe. Is that you or your roommate?"

"Me." She reached around the cubicle and handed me a container of shower gel. "Literature major."

"Really."

"Yup. You caught me. I'm a book nerd."

"Well, if that's the case I must be one too." I soaped up, relieved to wash the Walter stains off.

"Oh really. And what grants you access to the nerd club?"

I couldn't see her, but from the way she spoke, it sounded like she was smiling, and that was refreshing. "I just got my first book deal."

"You're a writer?" The awe in her voice was evident.

"No. I'm a barista who found some fool to publish my book," I replied. "Different thing."

"Don't be so modest. It's a big deal. Is it out yet? Would I have heard of it?"

"No and no," I said. "I only found out three days ago. The visit to New York was going to be a double celebration. My brother's new baby and my first published book." I squirted body wash onto my hands and rubbed it into my hair in lieu of shampoo.

"Bummer. Sorry about that. Awful timing."

"Story of my life."

"I'd love to write a book," Clara said. "That's why I came

here. This place has the best literature program in New England."

"It's a good thing you could afford it."

"Are you kidding? I couldn't afford this place in a million years. I worked my ass off to get a full scholarship, and I still ended up working in that shitty gas station four nights a week to survive." She turned the shower off. "Are you done in there?"

"Almost." I rinsed my hair and grabbed the towel.

"Good," Clara said. "I've been thinking. We should stay here tonight."

"I'm not sure that's a good idea." I wanted to reach New York and find my brother. This felt like an unnecessary delay.

"Come on, it makes sense. We spent last night on the floor. I don't know about you, but I hardly got a wink of sleep, especially with Walter tied up out front. We're exhausted. We have comfortable beds here and as much food as we want in the school kitchens."

"Well..." I still felt we should keep moving. On the other hand, a good night's sleep made sense.

"Just one night. We can use the time to plan our next move."

"One night." I pulled my boxer shorts on and stepped from the shower.

Clara was already dressed. She eyed me for a moment, her eyes dropping briefly to my boxers, and then she turned toward the door. "Great. We'll stay here tonight and move on in the morning."

I was about to answer her, but at that moment the lights flickered once, then twice, and went out.

CHAPTER FIFTEEN

THE ROOM PLUNGED INTO DARKNESS. The only light came from a small frosted glass window set high on the far wall.

"Shit," Clara swore.

"I was afraid this might happen." I had held out some small hope that things might not be as bad as they appeared. If the electricity was still on, then it meant there was someone keeping it that way. This latest development squashed that idea.

"I can't believe it. How much worse can things get?"

I sensed Clara was nearing a breaking point. "It doesn't matter. We can still spend the night here. It will be darker than I would have liked, but it's fine."

"I hate the dark," Clara said. "I always sleep with a nightlight."

"Maybe we can find a flashlight or something." I pulled the door open. "Come on, why don't we go back to the room. There's no point in staying here." Clara stood still for a moment, as if she was unsure what to do, and then pushed past me into the corridor.

We walked back to her dorm room, neither one of us speaking. When we arrived, she flopped down on the bed, staring sullenly at the ceiling.

I pulled on a fresh pair of jeans and a tee shirt, and made myself comfortable on the other bed.

The silence was like a gulf between us, a chasm that I couldn't cross. I wished there was something I could say or do to make her feel better, but I couldn't think of anything positive to say about our predicament. Instead, I said nothing.

We were still like that, lost in our own thoughts, when the first scream pierced the air.

Clara jumped up, a look of terror on her face. "What was that?"

"I don't know." I had assumed we were alone on the campus. It appeared I was wrong.

The second scream was worse.

"That sounded like it came from the quad," Clara said.

I ran to the window and peered out.

At first I saw nothing, but then there were two figures, a male and a female, running out from between the buildings and bolting across the open space. They looked scared. A moment later, I saw why. A group of fifteen or twenty men and women entered the quad. They moved fast, making a beeline for the couple. One pursuer, a large guy in a yellow tee, pulled ahead, closing the gap.

"Oh my God, I recognize some of those people." Clara was at the window now, her face pressed against the glass. "That guy in the yellow top, he's in my creative writing class. I think his name is Ben."

The fleeing couple reached the center of the open area. The smaller of the two, the girl, turned to glance over her shoulder. As she did so, her foot caught on something and she toppled forward, hitting the ground hard.

The guy stopped and hesitated for a moment, then raced back to help his stricken companion.

"You have to help them." Clara looked at me.

"I'll never get there in time."

"Please, we can't leave them out there like that."

"Alright. But lock the door behind me."

CHAPTER SIXTEEN

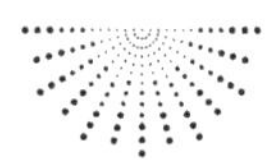

I TOOK THE STAIRS at a breakneck pace, jumping down the last four steps onto each landing and catapulting myself down the next flight. By the time I reached the bottom, I was winded, my lungs burning. I ignored my discomfort and raced across the lobby to the door leading to the quad and threw it open.

The man had pulled the woman to her feet, and by a miracle they were still ahead of the mob, but not by much. They were now moving away from me, across the grass toward the main building.

"Hey, over here!" I shouted, waving my arms to draw their attention.

They turned in my direction, and for a moment I saw confusion on their faces. Then they appeared to reach a mutual decision that there might be safety in numbers. They took off toward me at a clip, weaving in a wide arc to avoid their pursuers.

The mob turned and followed, shambling along at a fast pace. I watched them advance, saw their slack jawed expressions, and suddenly thought of my encounter with Walter back at the gas station. He had the same vacant, dead eyed look as these people.

The lights were on, but nobody was home.

If they caught this couple, I had a good idea what they would do.

"Come on. Hurry!" I shouted.

The couple ran headlong toward me, closing the gap. Unsure what else to do, I stepped outside, aware that I was now in as much danger as they were.

The mob was right behind them now. The guy in the yellow shirt whom Clara had identified as Ben was still leading. He stretched his arms out, hands grasping the air inches from his prey.

The man maneuvered himself behind his companion, using his body as a barrier between her and the mob, and then gave a mighty push. She stumbled forward into my arms.

I gripped her arms and retreated, pulling her through the door, and turned back for her companion. But it was too late. Ben was already upon him, dragging the terrified man backwards into the quad. My fingers brushed his outstretched hand, and then he was gone, consumed by the flailing arms of the mob.

For a moment, I lost him within the mass of crazed people. But then he reappeared, briefly amid the clawing, gouging pack. And all the while, his anguished cries of pain mingled with the dreadful sound of ripping and tearing and chewing.

"Rob!" The girl screamed her companion's name, tears flowing down her cheeks. She tried to push past me and get back to him, but I held on tightly, keeping her inside.

Ben broke away from the pack and turned, fixing us with bloodshot, dull eyes. His yellow shirt had taken on the copper red color of blood.

He took a step toward us.

I slammed the door.

CHAPTER SEVENTEEN

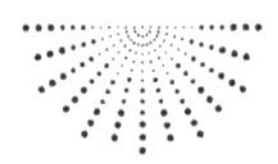

"THEY KILLED ROB." The girl sobbed, hysterical. She sat on the edge of the bed and rocked back and forth, her head in her hands. She would have been a pretty girl under different circumstances. Her cropped dark hair perfectly complimented an oval face and deep hazel eyes. I guessed she was about twenty years old. Her lithe build and toned features, along with the polo shirt bearing a hockey emblem, suggested that she played sports.

"We can't stay here." I glanced out of the window. The mob was still there, milling around the quad, walking in erratic circles. Occasionally, one would bump into another, and then a mild scuffle would break out until they veered away from each other. They reminded me of the dodgem cars at the fair. Except dodgems don't try to eat you.

"Well, we can't go out there," Clara said. "Not unless we want to be next on the menu."

"Agreed." It didn't look like any of them had attempted to break through the front door yet, which I'd secured with a hefty wooden bench dragged from the other side of the foyer. How long that would last was anyone's guess. "There must be another way out of the building, a back door."

"There's a service entrance that leads to the dumpsters. It's on the other side of the building."

"We can slip out that way. If we're lucky, they won't even see us."

"And what if we're not so lucky?"

"Then we run like hell."

"This is totally screwed up." Clara pulled a face.

"Yeah, it is. But nowhere near as screwed up as it will get if those-" I searched for the right words, "those crazy things get in here. They might act dumb right now, but I for one don't want to wait around until they get hungry again."

"Which brings me to my next question. What the hell happened to them?" Clara paced back and forth. "I know some of those people. I went to class with them, partied with them. They were nice people. Ben asked me out just last week."

"That doesn't matter right now."

"Don't tell me what matters. They ripped that poor guy to shreds. They were eating him. First Walter, and now this."

"Hey, keep it down." I motioned toward our guest.

"Sorry." Clara lowered her voice. She met my gaze. "I'm scared."

"Me too. But I'd rather move on and take my chances than wait in here. I might be wrong, but I don't think those things out there are in any hurry to leave."

"Where will we go?"

"Does it matter?" I felt a pang of disappointment. It would have been nice to have a comfortable bed for the night, but none of us would be able to sleep with the pack of crazies right below us. Besides, who knew when they would pull together some collective brains and go looking for another way inside? "It's not safe here anymore."

"It will be dark in a few hours."

"I know that. All the more reason to leave now while we still can." My eyes settled on the torn lump of ragged flesh and bone that was all that remained of Rob. The crazies had finished with him. They also seemed to have forgotten about us, at least for now.

"What about her?" Clara glanced toward the girl. "We can't go anywhere with her in that state."

"You're right." I turned to the girl and knelt down, taking her hand. "What's your name?"

She looked up; her face blotchy where tears had cut streaks through her makeup. "Emily."

"Pretty name." I squeezed her hand, speaking softly. "Listen, Emily, it's not safe here. We are going to find somewhere else to stay tonight. Do you understand me?"

"Yes." She sniffed and rubbed tears from her eyes.

"Good. That's very good."

"Rob's dead." Her bottom lip trembled, and I sensed I was losing her.

Clara knelt by my side. "Was he-" She paused, searching for the best way to ask. "Were you in a relationship?"

Emily shook her head. "No. He was the only person I could find after-" Her voice cracked. "They killed him."

"I know that, and I'm so sorry. I really am," I said. "But right now, I need you to take a deep breath and keep it under control. Focus on surviving. Do you think you can do that?"

Emily nodded.

"Fantastic." I turned to Clara. "Can you find some clothes that will fit her?"

"Yes. She looks about the same size as my roommate," Clara said, hopping to her feet.

"Do it. I want to be out of here in fifteen minutes."

"What if we run into more of those crazy people?"

"Don't worry about that." I picked up the crowbar from the bed, where Clara had discarded it when we arrived, and gave it a swing. "I played some baseball in college."

CHAPTER EIGHTEEN

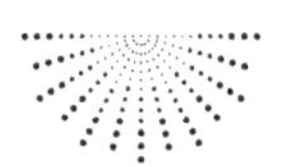

WE FLED THROUGH THE side door and down a narrow alley between the dormitory block and an adjacent building, then pushed through a fence behind the dumpsters.

I was on edge the whole time, but we didn't run into any more trouble, which was a good thing, because I wasn't confident that one measly crowbar was as great a weapon as I made it out to be. If confronted with a horde of crazies, we probably wouldn't fare too well, especially with Emily in tow. She had pulled herself together somewhat, but she looked like she could have another breakdown at any moment.

My stomach growled, reminding me that we hadn't eaten in hours, so I pulled a candy bar from my pack and ate it as we crossed a muddy field behind the college. Clara did the same, but Emily refused my offer of food, shaking her head and walking along in silence. The thought had crossed my mind, as we were preparing to flee, that our food supplies would be nowhere near enough to keep all three of us sustained for long. It also occurred to me that the college must have a well-stocked pantry with better options than chips and chocolate, but I wasn't willing to risk the time it would take to find and retrieve said food. Having seen what the crazies did to Rob, the last thing I wanted was to find myself backed into a walk-in cooler with ten or twenty of them clamoring at the door. Something bothered me though, and I asked Clara about it as soon as I felt we were far enough away from the college to ease up a little.

"How many students attend that college?"

She chewed the last of her candy bar and pushed the wrapper into her pocket. Even now, with the world gone to crap, she couldn't bring herself to litter. "I don't know, a thousand. Maybe more."

"What about the faculty?"

"Maybe another sixty or seventy. Why?"

"I was thinking about that mob in the quad. There couldn't have been more than twenty of them."

"So?"

"So where was everyone else?" I finished my snack. "I mean, if there were over a thousand faculty and students at the college when this all went down, where did they go? We didn't see a soul until that pack of crazies came onto the scene."

"Maybe they left, got out like we did."

"I don't think so. We walked all the way from the highway and didn't run across a single person. Surely we would have found a student or two somewhere along the way."

"What are you trying to say?" Clara asked.

"Things don't add up. There aren't enough people. Remember when we found that car near the off ramp?"

"Sure."

"It was locked."

"Doesn't mean anything. They could have gotten out and then locked it."

"Why would they? The car was totaled, the airbags deployed. It would be odd to lock the car up and walk off, leaving it there." I paused, letting this sink in. "Then there were the cars on the highway."

"We saw bodies on the highway." Clara went pale. "I don't think I'll ever forget that burned up guy."

"Right. We saw some bodies. But a lot of the vehicles were empty. True, some people might have gone crazy and wandered off like our friends back at the school, but some cars were so badly damaged, I'm not sure the doors would even open. And how do you explain that the seatbelts were still buckled with no one inside?"

Suddenly, Emily broke her silence. "They disappeared."

"Sorry?" As one, we turned to look at her.

"They were there, then they weren't." She stopped mid-step and turned to face us. "I was in the library studying when the headache started. I passed out. We all did, but when I woke up, I was alone. There were at least forty or fifty people in there with me, but they were just gone. Everything else was the same except for them. There were even books dropped on the floor as if people were holding them when they vanished."

"Maybe you were the last one to wake up," Clara said to Emily.

"Rob said the same thing," Emily said. "He was on his dorm floor playing video games with a bunch of friends, and when he woke up, he was alone. The other students, his friends, his roommate, all vanished."

"Just like the girl in the red dress back at the gas station," I said. "The one with the BMW."

"Come on. Disappearing people?" Clara said, a note of incredulity in her voice. "Aren't things weird enough without jumping to conclusions like that?"

"You tell me," I answered her. "All I know is that there appear to be a lot fewer people around than there should be."

"Listen to yourselves. That doesn't make sense. People don't just vanish."

"People go missing all the time," Emily said. "Haven't you ever seen the posters in the supermarkets or at police stations?"

"Not like this."

"Why not? It's just on a bigger scale now."

"And the crazies? What about them?" Clara said. "How do they fit into all of this?"

"I don't know. Maybe that's something else."

"Right. And maybe pigs fly." Clara turned and walked away, trudging down a slope toward a copse of trees at the edge of the field, without so much as a backward glance. "Let's keep moving, shall we?"

CHAPTER NINETEEN

EMILY SAW IT FIRST, a curl of dense smoke wafting up from beyond a cluster of tall trees.

We'd been following a narrow dirt road for what felt like forever, chatting sporadically, but mostly wallowing in our own thoughts. After the events at the college, we were all left a little shell-shocked. It wasn't every day you saw a person ripped to shreds in front of you.

"Maybe it's a campfire," Emily said. "There might be people."

"They might have food that isn't candy bars," Clara added. "I'm so hungry. What I wouldn't give for one of those gas station hot dogs now, piled high with chili and melted cheese."

"Ew." Emily wrinkled her nose. "Gross."

"Don't knock it if you haven't tried it," Clara retorted.

"I have tried it. Why do you think I said gross?"

"I don't think it's a campfire." I had been watching the smoke as we drew closer, and there was too much for something as innocuous as a campfire.

"Please tell me it's not another burned car," Clara said.

"It's not a car," I replied. We were approaching the trees,

drawing closer to the source of the smoke, and now I could see what it was. So could the others.

"A house," Clara said.

"At least it was a house before someone torched it." Emily slowed down, her eyes riveted on the smoldering structure.

"More like a farm." Beyond the destroyed house, I could see a patchwork of neatly tended fields separated by hedgerows. A path snaked back from the road to a large red barn that stood about a hundred feet away from us. A green tractor was in front of the house, and along the side of the barn were several pieces of equipment I could not identify.

"What do you think happened?"

"Who knows? Maybe crazies." I could see it all in my head, playing out like some B-rated movie. Mom in the kitchen cooking a meal ready for her husband when he comes home from the fields, the kids up in the bedroom playing with their Nintendo or on the computer. And then it happens. The headache. The blackout. Maybe the kids vanish like so many people seem to have done, or maybe they come down with a bad case of the crazies. In the kitchen, Mom has the gas going, pots on the stove and a roast in the oven, only now she's nuttier than a bag of almonds. She flails around, confused, bumping into things, knocking stuff onto the stove and the open flame. It only takes a moment to catch something alight. The rest, as they say, is history.

"What if there are crazies still here?" A look of panic crossed Emily's face.

"I don't think there is," I reasoned. By now we had reached the path leading to the barn, and there was no sign of life. "They likely burned up in the house, if there was anyone inside."

"I hope you're right." Clara eyed the crowbar.

"So do I." Now that I thought about it, I was not so sure.

"Shame it burned," Clara said. "Would have made a great place to stop for the night."

"We could stay there." Emily nodded toward the red barn.

"The barn?"

"Why not."

"It makes sense," I said. "There might not be another house for miles, and it's getting dark."

Clara didn't look convinced.

"Come on, let's check it out, and if it looks too bad, we'll move on."

"Fine." Clara stepped off the road onto the path.

At that moment, the barn door opened. A figure stepped out with a shotgun slung over one arm.

I froze.

Clara gripped my arm.

"That's far enough," said the figure in a deep bass voice. He raised the gun and aimed it directly at us. "If you take one more step, it'll be your last."

CHAPTER TWENTY

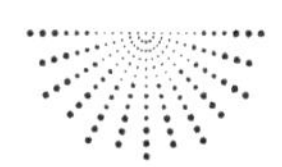

I POSITIONED MYSELF in front of the girls, acutely aware of the muzzle pointed at my chest. "We're not looking for any trouble."

"You can talk." A look of relief passed across the stranger's face. He kept the gun leveled on us. "You're normal."

"We are." I had never been on the receiving end of a gun before, and it was not a pleasant feeling. "Please, don't shoot."

"What's your business here?"

"We're looking for somewhere to stay for the night. We saw the barn and thought it might be a safe place to hole up." I still clutched the crowbar. Deciding it was best to look harmless, I placed it on the ground. "See, we're not armed."

"This here is my place. I got to it first," the stranger said, his eyes never straying from us. "Y'all need to move on, armed or not."

"We've been walking for hours," I pleaded.

"Not my problem, son."

Clara stepped out from behind me. "Please, we've been through so much. I can't go any further. We'll be on our way first thing in the morning. I promise."

"First thing, eh?"

"Yes. You have my word." She nodded.

"How do I know I can trust you?"

"You don't," Clara said. "But you're the one with the gun, not us."

"Good point, young lady." He finally lowered the weapon, much to my relief. "You don't have any of those zombie things on your tail, I assume?"

"No," I replied. "We ran into a bunch of them earlier today, but we gave them the slip."

"At least most of us did," Emily said under her breath.

"Ah hell, I might regret this later, but you better get in here." He motioned to us, speaking again when we didn't move fast enough. "Hurry. Before I change my damn mind."

CHAPTER TWENTY-ONE

TWO KEROSENE LAMPS lighted the barn with a soft yellow glow. Several hay bales were arranged like bench seats around a camping stove. A pot of soup bubbled away on top. It smelled so good that for a moment I almost forgot about our situation.

"Name's Clay. Clay Norton," our host said, perching himself on one of the bales. He propped up the shotgun, keeping it within easy reach.

"Hayden Stone," I said, offering Clay my hand. He looked at it as if deciding if I was worthy of a handshake, then grasped it and squeezed, the force of his grip almost crushing my fingers.

"Pleased to meet you, Hayden," Clay said, releasing me.

"This is Clara." I rubbed my sore palm. "And Emily."

"You're a lucky chap, travelling with a pair of beautiful girls like these. Yes sir, lucky indeed."

"Thanks." I eyed him, wondering if he was going to be trouble.

"Don't look at me like that boy," Clay said. "I'm not gonna cause you any grief. Unless you start something first, that is."

"We're not." I wished I'd retrieved the crowbar, but it was too late now.

"Alright then. You kids hungry? I got some chicken soup cooking and there's bread in that pack over there." He nodded toward a frame backpack near the door, the serious kind with metal supports, wide cushioned straps for hiking, and space for supplies, clothes and even a sleeping bag. "It's not much, but you're welcome to share it with me."

"Thank you." I let the girls sit down, and then positioned myself between them and Clay.

"You want a beer?"

"You have beer?" I asked. "I'd kill for a beer."

"Me too," Clara said.

Emily nodded.

"Don't joke." Clay stood and went to the backpack, pulling out a loaf of sandwich bread. He reached behind the pack and lifted a six-pack. "I killed for these here beers."

"You killed someone for a six-pack of beer?" Clara edged closer to me.

"Nah. More like four or five of the buggers," Clay said matter-of-factly. Then, seeing the look on our faces, he added. "Don't fret yourselves. It was zombies, and they were trying to have me for lunch."

"How many people have you killed in the last twenty-four hours?" I asked. It seemed to me that Clay was a little trigger-happy.

"A few." Clay passed the beers around. We each took one. "There was the group in the supermarket where I found the beer. I bagged another two up by the farmhouse."

"The burned one?"

"The same." He picked up four plastic throwaway cups and ladled soup into them, then handed one to each of us, keeping the fourth for himself. "Sorry about the choice of dinnerware, but beggars can't be choosers."

"It's fine. I'm just happy to eat something other than chocolate," I said. "So what happened to the house?"

"Don't know. It was like that when I got here." He twisted the cap off his beer and took a swig, smacking his lips in satisfaction. "Shame really. Would have been more comfortable than this place."

"Anything is better than spending the night outside." Clara ate her soup, dunking the sliced bread into the liquid and munching with vigor.

"Damn straight," Clay said. "Too many zombies running around out there."

"I wouldn't really describe them as zombies." He'd called them that a few times now. It was a little dramatic.

"Well, what in the hell do you call them, son?"

"Crazies."

"That's a piss poor name." He finished his soup and then helped himself to another beer. "Crazy don't eat people. Eatin' folk is a zombie thing; that's all there is to it."

"So what, you're some kind of an overnight expert on this stuff?" I asked.

"Reckon so."

"Let me guess. Because you go to Comicon every year?"

"No son, because I watched a gaggle of em' chew up some poor gal like she was their dinner buffet."

"Yeah. Well, join the club." An image of Rob, his arms reaching out for help, as they pulled him screaming into the throng raced through my mind.

"And because I put a bullet in the brain of every last one of them."

"I thought you said you only killed two groups. One at the grocery store, the other at the farmhouse."

"I did. I watched them eat that poor woman, then I popped em' all before I went shopping."

"You let them tear her apart and did nothing?"

"She was dead the moment they got their hands on her. Better they do the job quick than leave her to bleed out."

"Seems to me a bullet would have done the job quicker," I replied.

"I ain't no murderer, son. Zombies are one thing; normal folk, well, that's another kettle of fish."

"I was just saying..."

"Well, don't." Clay sipped his beer. "Killing a person is something you have to live with a very long time."

"Still, it would have been better to shoot her than let her get torn apart."

"Back seat driver, huh?" Clay smiled, although there was no mirth to the gesture. "You wait until you have to make that choice, then we'll see."

Emily sprang to her feet. "Stop it." She looked from me to Clay, her eyes wet with tears. "That's horrible. I don't want to listen to stuff like that."

"Hey, it's alright." I reached out and took her hand, pulling her back down. "We won't talk about it anymore."

"Good." She looked pale.

"I'm sorry." I met her gaze.

Clay looked down at the ground, ashamed. "Yeah. What he said."

"Thank you." Clara downed the last of her beer and pushed the bottle into the dirt. "Well, I don't know about the rest of you, but I want today to be over with. I think I'm going to find somewhere to lay my head and put it behind me."

CHAPTER TWENTY-TWO

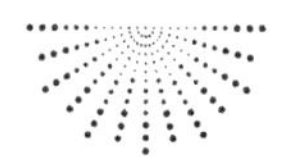

I SLEPT FITFULLY, drifting in and out of consciousness. Our accommodations were better than the previous night, but barely. Clara pulled a bale of hay to the back of the barn and spread it on the floor, creating a mattress of sorts, then put her pack under her head as a makeshift pillow. This was a good idea, so Emily and I followed suit, all three of us sharing the same space. Clay opted to sleep near the barn door, his shotgun resting on one arm. I wasn't sure if he was afraid of zombies, as he called them, or if he thought we might incapacitate him while he slept and steal his meager possessions.

Normally a beer would relax me enough to fall asleep easily, but not tonight. It was hardly surprising after what I had witnessed in the last twenty-four hours. Judging from Emily's unsettled tossing and turning, she was suffering from a similar affliction. Clara fell into a deep sleep almost immediately, which I envied.

Eventually my body won the fight with my mind and I fell asleep. I dreamed I was back on the highway, walking among the burned and wrecked vehicles, trucks with their contents spilled across the blacktop, cars crumpled and scorched. There were more bodies here now, and they refused to die despite horrendous injuries. I recoiled, backing away as they dragged themselves closer, broken limbs trailing behind, useless and grotesque. But it was their faces that scared me most, for I knew all of them. My brother and his wife, my parents, both of whom died years before, Clara and Emily, along with most of the other people I had known during my twenty-six years on the planet. Each hideous creature bore a recognizable face.

There was something else too, something that scared me more than the slowly approaching figures. A blackness hovered behind the crawling corpses. More than a shadow, but less than a shape. It felt threatening. I watched as it swept past the disfigured bodies and advanced toward me, features shrouded in dark obscurity. I tried to turn and run, but my feet refused to move. Panic rose from the pit of my stomach, and as the blackness reached for me, I screamed.

CHAPTER TWENTY-THREE

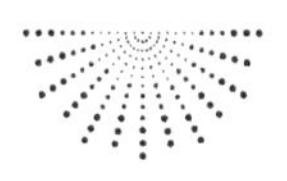

I JOLTED AWAKE, my heart pounding in my chest. My head was spinning, and my stomach felt like it had been kicked. All the stress and activity of the last twenty-four hours must have affected me more than I realized.

It was still dark.

Clara rolled over beside me and mumbled something unintelligible. I thought she might wake up, but she settled back down. On my left, Emily was curled up with her back to me, her knees drawn almost to her chest.

Once the dizziness receded, I rose. Careful not to disturb them, I took a bottle of water and slipped outside past Clay, who still cradled the shotgun. His loud, rhythmic snores spoke to the fact that he was clearly not adept at guarding the door. He also hadn't bothered to barricade it, or wedge it closed. Had a horde of crazies descended upon us while we slept, we would have found out as they were ripping us limb from limb. Not a pleasant thought.

It was cool outside. A slight breeze stirred the air, carrying with it the scent of freshly cut hay from the fields behind the barn. The farmhouse still smoldered, the fire's ashes glowing red in the darkness. With no electric lights to compete, the sky was alive with stars, the wide band of the Milky Way slashing across the heavens like a celestial river.

I twisted the top off the water and took a long drink. Standing outside, alone, with the barn door pulled almost closed until there was nothing but a crack between the door and the frame, I could almost believe that none of the events of the past few days were real. Everything looked so serene, so…

Normal.

Granted, there was a house not one hundred yards away that was now nothing more than a crispy shell, and if you believed Clay, and I did, there were a couple of bodies lying out in the darkness somewhere, two crazies with dime sized holes in their heads. But if you looked past that, glanced in any other direction, then the world was just as it always had been.

"Penny for your thoughts?"

I turned to find Clara leaning against the doorframe.

"Couldn't sleep," I said.

"Yeah. The end of the world will do that for you." She slipped outside and guided the door closed, careful not to let it bang.

"End of the world might be a bit harsh." I offered her some of my water. "Okay, nothing's working, no phones, no power, not even cars, and the highway looks like a wrecker's yard…"

"Don't forget the zombies." She took the water and gulped a mouthful down.

"Don't call them that."

"Why? Seems to fit."

"Zombies aren't real," I said. "I don't know what has happened to people, but I'm pretty sure they didn't turn into zombies."

"Whatever." She shrugged and handed the water back. "I've been thinking."

"Me too."

"We need a plan. Something to work toward. Otherwise,

we'll end up roaming around out here until the zombies..." She paused and corrected herself. "Sorry, the crazies get us."

"I know what my plan is."

"Really?"

"I need to find Jeff."

"Isn't your brother in New York?" Clara asked. "That's a long way without any transportation."

"I was thinking the same thing, but I have to try. He's all I have."

"He's probably dead already."

"Don't say that." I felt a prickle of anger.

"Look, I'm not being mean, but you have to realize that there's a good chance he didn't make it. New York is a prime target. I don't know what this thing is, but it seems like the city would be the first place hit. There are so many people there."

"You might be right, but what do I have to lose? There's nothing else left."

"That's not true. There's me." She reached out and touched my arm. "I need you."

I looked at her, momentarily dumbfounded. "What about your family?"

"I'm a realist. My parents live in Florida, and I have a brother out west. Unless a miracle happens, I can't reach any of them." She looked up at the sky, admiring the Milky Way. "You know, it's amazing to think how small we are, how tiny our planet is, and yet even on such an insignificant speck of rock we can be so far away from our loved ones."

"You will see them again," I said.

"Maybe." She fixed her attention back on me. "In the meantime though, I guess you're stuck with me."

"Well, there are worse people to be stuck with," I replied. "Clay, for a start. He'd probably have shot me by now."

Clara laughed, her eyes lighting up before a shadow fell over her face. "Why don't we go back inside? It's not safe out here."

"You're right. I don't know what I was thinking coming out here on my own." I reached out and gripped the barn door, holding it open for Clara to enter first.

At that moment, the phone in my pocket vibrated.

I looked at Clara, startled. "I think I just got a text."

"What?" She swiveled around, her eyes wide. "I thought the phones weren't working."

"Me too." I pulled the device from my pocket and turned the screen on, typing in the password. The text message icon had a bold number next to it. "I have a new text."

"Well?"

"Hang on." I opened it, waiting for the message to come up, and then read it, once to confirm who it was from, the second time to absorb the words, and then I turned to Clara. "We need to wake the others."

CHAPTER TWENTY-FOUR

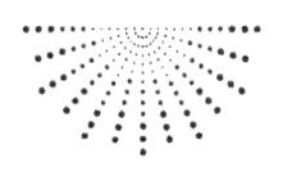

NEW HAVEN
GO SOUTH
VIRUS SPREADING

"What does it mean?" Emily looked down at the phone, her brow furrowed.

"It means I was right," Clay said. "Goddamned idiots in Washington went and started something they couldn't finish." He paced back and forth, a vein in his forehead throbbing. "I bet it's the Koreans, or the freaking Chinese. I knew it."

"Now hang on," I said. "We don't know anything."

"We know plenty," Clay replied. "Virus spreading? That can only mean one thing. Biological warfare."

"That's jumping to conclusions," Clara said. "We're as much in the dark as we were yesterday."

"No, we're not. Those things, those zombies, they are infected with a damn virus."

"And it's spreading," Emily said. "At least if you believe the text message."

"On the face of it we have no reason not to." Clara looked at me. "Are you sure it was your brother who sent it?"

"Sure as I can be." I picked up the phone. "It's from his number."

"Does New Haven mean anything to you?" Clara asked.

"No."

"It would be nice if the message gave us a bit more information," she said. "The only New Haven I know of is in Connecticut."

"Connecticut seems logical, given our location," I agreed. "And Jeff might be there if they evacuated New York."

"Which would explain the text." Clara looked hopeful.

"Kind of," Clay said. "But it doesn't explain everything."

"What?" I looked at him.

"How come your phone works when no one else's does?" Clay narrowed his eyes. "Seems mighty odd to me."

"I don't know. When I charged it at the school, there was no service."

"And now?"

"A weak signal. One bar."

"One bar, huh, all the way out here in the middle of nowhere. Have you called the number back?" Clay asked. "Replied to the text message?"

"First thing I did. The text bounces back undeliverable, and the number gets an automated message. The call cannot be completed at this time."

"And yet somehow you got that text through anyway," Clay said, narrowing his eyes.

"I never said I had all the answers." I wasn't sure what Clay was getting at, but he was annoying me.

"We're getting off point here." Clara positioned herself between us, sensing the change in mood. "The issue is, what do we do next?"

"I say we do what the phone said and go south," Emily piped up.

"I agree." I was tiring of the discussion. "We should head toward New Haven. If this message is from Jeff, then he must be there already. It must be safe."

"There's no guarantee the message meant New Haven, Connecticut." Clay wanted to argue. "Seems like a waste of time if you ask me."

"Well, we're not asking. Come with us, or don't. No skin off my nose."

"Easy there, fella." Clay turned to Clara. "Sensitive one, ain't he, your boyfriend."

"He's not my boyfriend." Clara shot me a look. "But he's right. We can't stay here, and New Haven seems as good a place to go as any."

"If you're smart, you'll head toward the border," Clay said. "Canada."

"Why on earth would we want to go there?" I asked, wondering if Clay had lost his mind. "What makes you think Canada will be any different from here?"

"Of course it'll be different. It's Canada." Clay drew a breath. "Whatever this is, this thing that's happened, the chances are that it was an attack on the USA. We're always poking our noses in where they don't belong. Maybe someone got mad and poked back. I bet Canada is fine."

"If it is, and that's a big if, they will have closed the border by now. What are you going to do? Waltz on up there and ask them to let you in?"

"Pretty much."

"Good luck with that." I turned to Clara and Emily. "I vote we make our way south, go to New Haven."

"I agree," Clara said.

"Me too." Emily nodded.

Clay looked us over, as if trying to figure out if we were

really serious, then shrugged. "Hey, it's your funeral." He turned and stomped off, then returned with a pistol. "If your hell bent on heading south, you'd better take this."

"I don't know." I hesitated.

"Just take it, numb nuts. You're going to need something to defend yourselves with." He pressed the gun into my hand. "When this is all over I expect you to find me and give it back, comprende?"

"Sure."

"Well, alright then." Clay grinned.

I looked down at the pistol, solid and heavy in my hand. Now we were armed.

CHAPTER TWENTY-FIVE

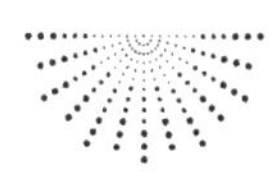

"DO YOU THINK he'll make it to Canada?" Emily asked as we walked along.

"I don't know. Maybe. I hope so." We'd left Clay behind at the barn several hours before and trekked over the fields, finally linking back up with the highway. Much as I wanted to avoid the Interstate, with its mangled cars and dead bodies, it was also the quickest way to travel. My one concern was running into more crazies, and the closer we were to civilization the more chance we had of encountering them. Despite this, the day had so far proven uneventful, and the Interstate, which had been clogged with cars the last time we walked it, was surprisingly free of vehicles. We went long stretches with barely a wreck to be seen, much to my relief. When we came across a vehicle or a pileup, we gave it a wide berth, wary of what, or who, might be lurking out of sight.

"We shouldn't have left him there like that, all alone," Clara said. "It's not right."

"He made his choice." A part of me wished Clay had come with us. He clearly knew his way around firearms, and that shotgun of his would come in useful when we ran into more crazies, which I was sure we would. On the other hand, I found myself leery of him. It wasn't anything I could put my finger on, but I had a feeling he would be bad news if we stuck with him for too long.

"Even so–"

"I didn't like him," Emily said. "He didn't make me feel safe."

"Me either." It seemed I wasn't the only one who had taken a dislike to Clay.

"You know, he gave us a gun."

"He did. I'm still not sure why." I reached down to my belt and touched the handle of the pistol. In my pocket I had a handful of bullets, which Clay gave to us as we were preparing to leave. Since I was the only one with any firearms experience, I kept the gun while Clara took the crowbar. Emily found a wicked looking old rake with three curved tines at the back of the barn and kept it. It was rusty, and the handle was snapped off halfway down, but it was better than nothing.

"Maybe he felt bad for us." Clara hitched her backpack higher, repositioning it.

"Maybe." It didn't matter. We were walking in opposite directions.

"How long do you think it will take us to get to New Haven?" Emily asked.

"It's a pretty long trek." I had been wondering about that myself. "Several days, at least."

"I wonder if there are other people out there like us, people that didn't get infected with the virus?"

"I hope so." There were several towns along the way. Surely someone must have survived. The big question was whether the survivors would be friendly. Even Clay had come out pointing a gun at us, and if there were crazies running around, it might tempt people to shoot first and ask questions later.

"There are other survivors," Clara said as we approached yet another off ramp, this one blocked by a semi–trailer that had veered from its lane and jack knifed, spilling pallets of building materials across the road. "Look."

I followed her gaze. At first I saw nothing, but then my eyes settled on a motel a few hundred yards off the exit. On the roof of the office, a bed sheet was spread out, with one word written across it in big, bold lettering.

HELP.

CHAPTER TWENTY-SIX

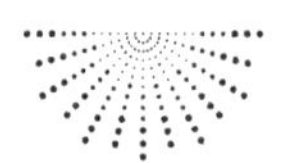

THE PINELAND COURT MOTEL looked like it hadn't received a fresh coat of paint in thirty years. The rooms, arranged in three blocks surrounding a central parking lot, looked drab and old, with ugly under window air conditioners and walkways enclosed with rusted railings. Several of the bedroom doors stood open to various degrees, revealing black, murky interiors. A neon sign, now dark, sat atop a long metal pole next to the road. I wondered if it would work even if there were any power, which there clearly was not. It appeared that the entire state was out.

Next to the motel, attached by a short connecting corridor, was a restaurant as dilapidated as the rest of the place. A painted sign mounted on the roof identified the place as Donny G's Steakhouse and Diner–open 24 hours seven days a week. Faded posters in the window advertised $6.99 steaks, Meatloaf Tuesdays and a $3.99 cheeseburger. Ordinarily I avoided places like this. But right now, a cheap steak from a greasy spoon sounded like heaven on earth.

The buildings appeared to be deserted. Apart from a couple of cars in the parking lot, and another with its front end crumpled into a lamppost in front of the restaurant, there was no sign of life. As we walked closer, however, it became clear that something bad had gone down over the last two days.

"Is that what I think it is?" Emily was the first to see the dark red smears on the glass doors of the registration area. Beneath them, on the concrete, a long wide streak led into the road and abruptly ended. A lone tennis shoe, once white but now stained crimson, lay on its side in silent testimony to the violent place the world had become in just forty-eight short hours.

"I think so." I hoped that whoever owned the shoe had not suffered much, but I had a feeling that they did. An image of Rob and his agonizing screams as the crazies tore him limb from limb in the college quad flashed into my mind.

"It might not be safe here." Clara looked around, nervous.

"The blood's not fresh; this happened a while ago," I said. "And anyway, whoever wrote that message on the roof might still be here."

"Or they could be the owner of that shoe."

"A distinct possibility." She had a point. Still, we should at least try to find out. Besides, there was a restaurant next door, and that meant we could stock up on food and water, which we desperately needed. I stepped past the abandoned shoe and pulled on the office door. It rattled, but didn't open. "Locked."

"Let's take what we need and move on," Clara said. "There's no one here."

I cupped my hands to the glass and peered through, careful to avoid the smeared blood, but the interior was so dark I could make out very little. I turned away from the door, disappointed. "Let's check out the restaurant."

"Finally," Emily said. "I'm starving."

The three of us made our way past the lobby parking area and across a rectangle of patchy grass to the restaurant.

Clara immediately pulled on the double doors, shaking them. "These are locked too."

"We'll have to find another way in," I said. Maybe there was a service entrance, or an open window.

"No need." Clara hoisted the crowbar and slipped it into the gap between the doors, just above the lock, and pushed sideways. The doors parted a little, but remained steadfast.

She pushed again, grunting with the effort.

For a moment I thought the doors would hold, but then they emitted a mighty creak, followed by a sharp crack, and swung inward.

Clara grinned. "Voila."

"Wow." I looked at her with newfound admiration. "Where did you learn to do that?"

"My father taught me. He used to jack jewelry stores when he was younger. Now he mostly does bank jobs."

"Really?"

"No, of course not. God, you're gullible." She punched my arm. "My father is an engineer in Boca Raton."

"Oh."

"Come on." She stepped across the threshold into the restaurant.

Emily followed suit, glancing sideways as she passed me. "So gullible."

I stood there for a moment, bemused.

Clara turned to me. "Well, are you coming or not?"

"Yes. Of course." I hurried inside and instantly recoiled.

The smell was pungent, a combination of decomposing meat and rotten vegetables. Some of the odor was surely coming from a salad bar on the back wall, still stocked with a selection of lettuce, tomatoes, and several tubs of dressing, though the fare was past edible. Even if it had been in any condition to consume, the swarm of buzzing flies would have been more than enough to put me off. More flies circled a few half-eaten dinner plates on a table near the door behind the hostess stand.

"Ew." Emily wrinkled her nose. "It smells like ass in here."

"Better get used to it," I said. "With the power out, any food that isn't pre-packaged will go rotten, and it will only get worse. We'll run into this more and more."

"Perfect." She swatted a lone fly away from her face. "Suddenly, I'm not hungry anymore."

"The kitchen must be through here." I stepped toward a set of double swing doors inset with two small round windows. "If there's anything useable it will be in there."

"We should be careful what we take," Clara said. "We can only carry so much."

"We can ditch most of the snack food we took from the gas station. It's all sugar anyway."

"Not all of it," Emily said. "Sugar is good if we need a sudden burst of energy. I watched a documentary on TV last year that said chocolate is a good emergency ration. Soldiers use it as part of their survival kit."

"We'll keep the chocolate then."

"And the beef jerky," Clara chimed in. "Easy source of protein."

"Fine, the jerky stays too," I said, pushing through the doors. They swung back in place after us. "But the chips are history."

"Suits me." Clara shrugged. "Too fattening."

"Really? You're worrying about your weight at a time like this?"

"Hey, I'm still a girl," Clara replied, wandering deeper into the kitchen. "Even if I can jimmy a lock better than you."

"Funny. Real funny." I saw a long-bladed carving knife on one of the prep counters and picked it up, then decided that it was too much trouble to carry safely. I put it down again next to a cluster of yellowed and odorous raw chicken breasts that never made it as far as the skillet. "There must be a pantry here somewhere."

"What about that?" Emily pointed to a heavy silver door set into the wall next to a row of shelves that held commercial sized tins of tomato sauce, mayonnaise, cooking oils, and various salad dressings.

"That should do it." A heavy-duty latch secured the door, keeping it closed. I gripped it, depressed the button on the underside of the mechanism, and pulled.

The door opened easily, swinging outward to reveal an oversized walk-in with metal racks lining both sides. The racks contained an assortment of foods. Fresh produce, vegetables and fruits packed into open top cardboard boxes occupied one section. Next to that were several blocks of cheese and a large package of grated cheddar, while on the other side meats filled the shelves. Hamburgers separated by small grease paper sheets, steaks in tubs labeled rib eye sirloin and flank.

This was not a pantry, but a walk in cooler. The food was in better shape than the stuff left out on the counters, but without electricity to keep the room chilled, it was already going bad.

However, it was not the food that held my attention. It was the woman crouched in the corner between the racks.

CHAPTER TWENTY-SEVEN

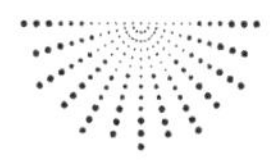

"HEY, THERE'S SOMEONE BACK HERE," I said, approaching the figure.

"What?" Clara pushed up next to me. "Oh, my God. Is she alive?"

"I don't know. I can't tell." Her back was turned to us, making it almost impossible to see if she was breathing. "She isn't moving. I wonder how long she's been stuck in here."

"Maybe she's the person who wrote that message on the roof." Emily craned to see past us.

"What would she be doing in a cooler, though?" Something wasn't right. The woman still hadn't moved, but a sense of unease was settling over me.

"She could have taken refuge in here when things went wrong," Clara said, then bending close, she spoke to the woman. "Hello? Can you hear me? Are you hurt?"

There was no movement.

"She might be dead," I said. "If she came in here while the power was still on, this room would be freezing."

"We need to make sure." Clara crept forward and reached out, touching the woman on the shoulder.

The woman spun sharply, glaring at us with bloodshot eyes. Gobs of thick spittle frothed at the corners of her mouth and trickled down her chin.

"Oh shit." Clara squealed and pulled her hand back, half falling out of the cooler.

The woman pulled herself up, mouth open, baring blood-stained teeth. She made odd grunting sounds, deep and guttural, inhuman. A badge attached to her soiled uniform sported the name Alice.

And then she lunged.

Alice shot forward so fast it took me a moment to realize what was happening. Her hands flailed at me, her nails grazing the skin of my cheeks, fingers clutching for the collar of my shirt.

I twisted free, leaving a ripped clump of material in Alice's possession. I stumbled backward, at the same time reaching for the cooler door, and slammed it closed with all my might.

It almost worked. At the last second, an arm shot through the gap. The door bounced off with a sickening crunch of bone, preventing it from closing.

Emily screamed.

I put my shoulder to the door and pushed back, holding it in place, ignoring the slightly rubbery resistance provided by the trapped arm.

I gritted my teeth and set my feet, determined not to let her out, but unsure exactly what to do next. If I eased up on the pressure, she would slip through the gap, but I couldn't latch the door again with Alice's arm pinned the way it was. I looked around, frantic, for something to wedge the heavy door in place, thus freeing me to make my escape. But there was nothing.

"What now?" I asked Clara, hoping she would have some idea what to do next.

The door shuddered as Alice threw herself against it, determined to escape her makeshift cell.

"I don't know." Clara looked confused.

"Well, we need to come up with something. I'm not sure how long I can hold on here." I could feel my shoulder going numb.

"Why don't we cut the arm off," Emily said, eyeing a nasty-looking meat cleaver hanging from a hook above a prep station. "That would fix it."

"What?" Both Clara and I looked at her.

"If we chop it off, we can close the door. Problem solved."

"And who's going to do that, you?" I retorted, bracing as Alice slammed her body against the door again with a bellow of rage. "Because I sure as hell have no intention of cutting anyone's arm off."

"Well–" Emily bit her bottom lip.

"Exactly."

"We're going to have to let her out," Clara said, summing the situation up. "We don't have a choice."

"There must be another way." I was being stubborn, I knew, but the last thing I wanted to do was let this madwoman loose. I still remembered the run-in with Walter back at the gas station, and Alice acted even more insane.

"You can't stay there forever. Eventually you will get too tired to hold her back."

"I know." The same thought had occurred to me.

"Forget the door. Leave it," Clara pleaded. "We need to get out of here. We need to run. It's our only chance."

"Fine. When I say run, we run." I wished I had never opened the cooler, but it was too late for that. "Ready?"

"Ready." Clara gripped my arm.

"Me too." I could sense the fear in Emily's voice.

"Okay then," I said, keeping my eyes fixed on Alice. "On three. One, two, three - Run!"

I jumped away from the door as Alice hit it once again. She flew through, stumbling to stay on her feet, seemingly oblivious to the way her mangled arm now hung at the wrong angle. The pain should have been incredible, but she ignored the damaged limb and fixed her gaze upon us instead.

Not waiting to see what she did next, I turned and fled, following the girls, who were already racing back the way we'd come, toward the swing doors that opened into the dining room.

Alice let out a shriek of anger and gave chase, her flailing arms sending food and plates and bowls crashing to the ground.

I caught up with Clara and Emily as they reached the doors. Alice was coming up fast from behind, running with a weird lopsided gait. She was gaining on us with a speed that was as shocking as it was surprising, given her age. Under other circumstances, she would have given an Olympic sprinter a run for their money.

We barreled into the dining room and sprinted toward the front door, with the crazed server right behind us. Just as we were about to reach the door, a voice called out to us.

"Not that way!" I turned to see a tubby kid in his late teens waving at us from a set of doors at the far end of the restaurant. A sign on the wall next to the doors read, *To Hotel Lobby.*

"Over here. Quick!" The kid was practically jumping up and down. "This way."

Clara and Emily had also seen him. They veered to the left, barely avoiding the manic Alice, and ran in his direction. I was not so lucky.

Alice flew toward me, screeching and growling.

If she caught me I would be dead, of that there was no doubt. Even though she was about forty pounds lighter and thirty years older than me, the sheer scale of her rage gave her the advantage. I plucked a chair from the nearest table and rushed forward. The legs caught her square in the chest, sending her reeling backward. She lost her balance and fell.

Clara and Emily were already at the door. They hovered there, waiting for me to catch up.

"Come on." Clara motioned for me to run. "Quickly, before she gets back up."

I didn't need to be told twice. I darted forward, leaping over the stricken Alice. She reached upward to grab ahold of me, but her hands closed on the empty air where I had been a second before.

I ran toward the door, dodging tables and chairs along the way. When I reached the girls, I practically pushed them through.

No sooner were we clear than the tubby kid slammed the doors shut and rammed a piece of old pipe through the handles.

Just in the nick of time.

The doors shuddered and flexed inward as Alice, back on her feet, crashed into them in an attempt to follow us. The makeshift barricade held tight, much to her obvious displeasure.

"That was too close." I drew huge gulps of air, trying to catch my breath, and leaned against the wall, thankful to be alive.

CHAPTER TWENTY-EIGHT

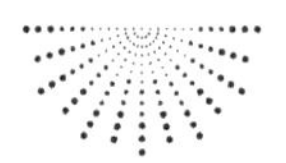

"WHAT WERE YOU DOING IN THERE?" The tubby kid demanded. "You could have gotten yourselves killed. More to the point, you could have gotten me killed."

"What were we doing?" I replied, incredulous. "What were you doing with a waitress in a cooler?"

"That's Alice." The kid replied matter-of-factly.

"No shit." I wanted to slap him.

"You let her out." The kid led us along a short corridor and into the hotel lobby. "Do you know how long it took me to get her in there?"

"Why would you lock her in a cooler in the first place?"

"What else was I going to do? She went crazy." He flopped down on a sofa in a small lounge area to the right of the registration desk and put his feet up on a pine coffee table. "Name's Darwin."

"Well, thank you for saving us back there, Darwin," Clara said.

"No biggie."

"You know, Darwin, you could have put a note on that freezer door warning us what was inside," I said. "It would have saved an awful lot of trouble."

"I wasn't expecting anyone to bust in to the restaurant and start poking around, was I?" Darwin shook his head. "Man, you messed things up."

"I'm not sure why you locked her up in the first place," I said. "Why didn't you kill her?"

"Why didn't you?" Darwin was looking at my waist. "You have a gun."

"Good point." The pistol had slipped my mind in the excitement. I felt a little sheepish, not that I was sure I would have been able to pull the trigger. It was one thing to bop a guy over the head with a propane tank or knock someone over with a chair, but shooting them was a whole other ballgame.

Emily took a seat on a chair opposite Darwin and spoke to him. "Are you the only one here?"

"Yeah." He sniffed and rubbed his nose with the back of his hand. "I was working the night shift and I must have passed out. When I woke up, everything was really weird. Been that way ever since. At first I thought it was me."

"You?" I was confused.

"Yeah. You know." He reached into his pocket and brought out a hand-rolled cigarette, only it wasn't tobacco. "It gets real boring here. This stuff helps me pass the time."

"Weed?"

"Right on. You want one?" He produced a second joint and held it out. "Anyone? I have plenty."

"No, I don't want one."

"And neither do we." Clara glared at him.

"Suit yourselves. It'll make you feel better. Takes the edge off things. If it wasn't for this stuff, I don't know what I'd have done the last few days. It's been kind of lonely here." He glanced toward the door. "There was this one guy came around yesterday morning, started hollering to let him in. I think he might have been a guest here. He didn't make it though. That's how I found out about Alice."

"She killed him?" I remembered the bloody streaks on the door, the lone tennis shoe.

"Oh yeah." Darwin shuddered. "Not a pleasant sight. Tore him up with her bare hands."

"Why didn't you let him in?" I asked.

"Too late. By the time I realized he was outside, Alice was already munching on him like he was one of her meatloaf specials. I don't think he even saw it coming, poor guy."

He put the joint between his lips and pulled a box of matches from his pocket.

"You're going to smoke that now?"

"Sure. Why not?"

"Because there's a crazy waitress with a hankering for human flesh running around outside, and we need you level headed." I reached out and plucked the joint away, then threw it into the nearest trashcan. "Speaking of which, we need to figure out the food situation since we can't get back into the restaurant."

"Oh, that's easy." Darwin looked wistfully toward the trashcan, then back to me. "I've got a bunch of food in the office."

"You do?"

"Yeah. I moved most of the useable stuff out of the kitchen after I locked Alice in the cooler. It seemed like the safest thing to do. Who knows how many other nut jobs like her are roaming around out there."

Clara grinned. "Darwin, you just made my day."

CHAPTER TWENTY-NINE

DARWIN WOULD HAVE MADE a good squirrel. Enough food and drink filled the office to keep a small army on its feet. Restaurant supply boxes packed full of tortilla chips, large bottles of salsa, several varieties of soup, at least three dozen loaves of sandwich bread, and pickles galore littered the floor. There were family sized bags of Doritos, one of which was open, its contents spilling onto the desk, and a myriad of other goodies.

"There was meat and cheese too. I ate some of it the first day, but after the power went out I didn't want to chance it," he said. "It was a shame to waste it, but I didn't want to get sick."

"This looks like a feast after what we've been eating," I said. Clay had generously shared his meal the previous evening, giving us a much-needed break from candy bars and assorted bags of nuts. However, with only a small pot of soup and bread to feed four people, our hunger had returned within a few hours. This veritable Aladdin's cave of munchies was like hitting the mother lode.

"Ooh, Coco Krispies." Clara's eyes alighted on a stack of

cereal boxes next to the door. "I haven't had those since I was a kid."

"No milk though," Darwin said. "Sorry."

"Who needs milk?" She grabbed a box and pried it open, then scooped up a handful of the chocolate cereal, eating with gusto. Then, realizing we were all watching her, she stopped. "What? You've never seen a girl eat cereal before?"

I grinned. "Not quite like that."

"Well, now you have." She dug deep again, coming out with another handful of the small brown pebbles. She held the box in my direction. "Want some?"

"Nah. I think I need something a bit more balanced than chocolate cereal." I picked up a banana and peeled back the skin, then took a bite.

"Suit yourself." Clara dipped into the box again. "But you don't know what you're missing."

CHAPTER THIRTY

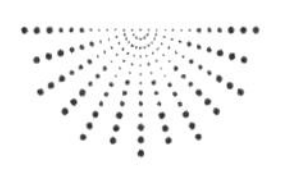

OUR BELLIES FULL, we turned to the more serious matter of where to sleep for the night. It didn't seem like a good idea to push on further down the road, especially with dusk approaching. Besides, it would be a shame to pass up the chance for a good night's sleep in a bed. The only problem was that the motel lacked inside corridors, meaning we would be more vulnerable than we were in the lobby. After much debate, we agreed that the best course of action would be to take two rooms on the second floor. We came to this conclusion because the ground floor rooms were vulnerable to attack and hard to defend, especially with Alice still on the loose.

We selected rooms linked by an interior door. Even though we only intended to use one room, the connecting doors provided a second means of escape should anything happen. We took the time to barricade the stairs with a couple of dressers, and we made a thorough search of all the rooms on that floor, lest any hotel guests were still lurking around with crazy fever.

Darwin had spent the last few nights in the lobby, sleeping behind the reception desk, but now he decided it would be safer to stick with us. Four people sharing two beds in one room was not ideal, especially since the beds were only queen sized, but I didn't think it would be a good idea to use both rooms, and the girls agreed.

Darwin and I took the bed closest to the door, which meant that Clara and Emily would share the other bed. After the sleeping arrangements of the last few evenings, the motel room was pure luxury. After a brief discussion, we decided that Darwin and I would take turns keeping watch on the balcony outside the room, switching over in four-hour shifts. That Darwin was a pothead did concern me, so we made him turn out his pockets, and we confiscated all the joints we found. After that, with the light fading fast, we settled in for the night.

CHAPTER THIRTY-ONE

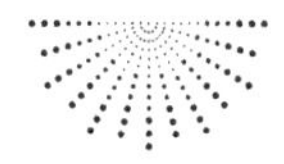

THE MOON WAS HIGH and full in the night sky. I leaned on the second floor railing and looked up at it, transfixed for a moment. Were other survivors out there looking up at the same moon right now? More to the point, was Jeff looking at it all those miles away in New Haven? I hoped so.

My mind wandered to the unlikely text message. Why was I the only one to receive one? Was it really from Jeff? I did not know. It was his number, but that only meant someone had his phone. Hardly rock solid evidence of his survival, especially since the connection only worked one way. For all I knew, there was nothing waiting for us in New Haven. Or worse, we were walking into a trap. What other choice did we have? We had to take the chance. We couldn't stay where we were, and south was as good a direction to go as any. Maybe they had power. Maybe things were normal down there.

"Any sign of trouble?"

I turned to find Clara standing there. She quietly pulled the door to within a crack of closed and joined me at the railing.

"Not so far," I replied. "I haven't heard or seen a thing in hours, unless you count a cat that ran across the parking lot about thirty minutes ago."

"Good." She hugged herself. Once the sun had gone down, the temperature was chilly for the time of year.

"You should be sleeping."

"I tried," she said. "I lay there for over an hour staring at the ceiling. My mind won't shut off. Darwin's snoring didn't help much either."

"He snores?"

"Like a freight train."

"That sucks. Sorry about that."

"Just my luck. Emily didn't seem to notice. She fell asleep almost as soon as her head hit the pillow." Clara paused for a moment, as if trying to decide if she should continue. "What do you think about Darwin?"

"He seems okay. A little flakey perhaps."

"Yeah." She blew on her hands and rubbed them together. "I think we should be on our guard when we come across new people. We've been lucky so far, but there might be others out there with less altruistic motives."

"I was thinking the same thing. When we found that barn yesterday, I was sure Clay was going to shoot us. Thank the stars he had the good sense not to shoot first and ask questions later."

"Next time we might not be so fortunate. If people are encountering those crazies, they might not want to chance it."

"Food is going to get pretty scarce too. I don't know how many survivors there are, but at some point they are going to start squabbling over provisions," I said.

"That thought occurred to me too."

"We might have to defend ourselves from more than crazies." I touched the butt of the pistol.

"I don't want to think about that," Clara said. "Can we talk about something else?"

"Like what?"

"Well, how about your book? The one you are going to get published."

"You mean the one I was going to get published. I doubt the offer still stands under the circumstances." I felt a pang of regret at those words. For the first time it hit me that my labor of love, the novel I'd spent countless hours slaving over for almost two years, would never sit on a bookstore shelf, or reach the best-seller lists, or even have a single reader other than myself.

"Tell me about it, the book." Clara moved closer, her arm brushing against mine. "What's it called?"

"Promise you won't laugh?"

"Why would I?" she said.

"When Dreams Were Done." I spoke the name of the book, and that flicker of disappointment returned. "It's a mix of fantasy and love story set in the twenties. My stab at literary fame."

"Sounds interesting."

"You haven't read it yet."

"I'd like to." She looked at me. "When this is all over."

"This might never be over," I said. "Besides, I left my laptop locked in the car's trunk back at the gas station."

"Too bad."

"What about you? How did you see your life going?"

"Not like this, obviously. I'm not sure I had any concrete plans after school. I took literature because I love books, not because I had any great ideas for my future. Sounds kind of shortsighted, huh?"

"Not really. I've spent the last three years serving coffee. Hardly a stellar career move."

"But you also wrote a book."

"Yes. I did. And look where that got me." I surveyed the motel parking lot again.

"It brought you to me. If you weren't still working in that

coffee shop, you might not have pulled into the gas station when you did." She closed her hand over mine. "I'm not sure I would have made it this far without you."

"Are you kidding me?" I said. "You'd have done fine without me. I saw the way you busted the restaurant door open like a pro."

"Ah yes. My father taught me well." She laughed, her eyes dancing, before a look of sadness came upon her. "They're dead, aren't they? My parents."

"Maybe." It was futile to lie. "Then again, we're not. If they survived, they're likely thinking the same thing about you."

"You are lucky. You know your brother is fine."

"All I know is that his phone sent me a text, and a pretty impersonal one at that. Anyone could have sent it."

"For what purpose?"

"I don't know."

"You should choose to believe it was your brother that sent it until you find out otherwise. Everyone needs a little hope."

"And what about you?" I asked. "What hope do you have?"

"I hope we reach New Haven and it's a safe place, somewhere with normal people. Who knows, maybe my parents are heading there right now, just like us."

"You're right." I put my arm around her.

"I know." She rested her head on my shoulder and closed her eyes. Suddenly there didn't seem to be anything else worth saying. It was enough to be close, to share the moment, two small specs of humanity huddling together under the heavy moon. Who knew what lay ahead, what tomorrow would bring? But for now we had each other - and a little dash of hope.

CHAPTER THIRTY-TWO

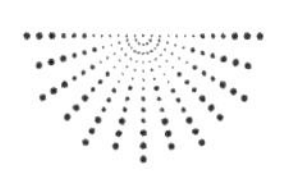

CLARA STAYED WITH ME on the balcony for a while longer before retiring back to the room. Before she left, she made me promise not to stay up all night keeping watch, to let Darwin take his turn. Apparently, she sensed my unease about the pothead guarding us, but she also knew I would need to be rested for the next day.

The silence was like a void after she left, and I found my mind drifting. With Darwin not set to relieve me for another hour, I paced back and forth, doing my best to stay alert and fight the boredom. Since freeing Alice from the cooler, we had not seen her once, which made me uneasy. I took a turn up and down the balcony to see if I could locate her.

The walkway ran around three sides of the parking lot, rusting iron railings guarding the edge. I set off at a slow pace, aware that with every step I was moving further away from help should I need it, further out of earshot. I reached the first bend and paused, scanning the way ahead. The stairs we had barricaded earlier disappeared into darkness to my left, and I glanced nervously toward them, half expecting to see Alice there in her bloody apron, but all I saw were the dressers and other assorted pieces of furniture we'd piled up to block the stairwell. I continued on, wishing the electricity still worked, or that I had a flashlight, anything to illuminate the way ahead. I was almost at the second corner when I saw it. A slight movement near the edge of the parking lot, toward the road. It was nothing much, barely anything at all really, but it was enough to draw my attention.

I stopped and peered over the railing, my eyes searching the gloom, but I failed to find anything out of place. Thinking that it must have been my over active imagination I was about to turn away, but then it came again, a shifting of the darkness.

The hairs on the back of my neck stood up. We were not alone. I reached down, my hand finding the pistol in my belt, and drew it out, just to be safe, my eyes never leaving the road.

I could see it now, a shape shuffling along, cloaked in darkness. It might have been Alice, but somehow I knew it was not. There was something masculine about the gait, and even though I could not see much, I saw enough to know the build was wrong for a woman.

The man followed the line of the road, never once veering into the parking lot. When he reached the midpoint between the buildings, he stopped and looked up.

I shrank back, nervous that the newcomer would see me and move toward us. Despite this, a part of me wondered if this was another lost soul, someone who had woken up to find the world a strange new place full of nasty things; someone as scared as I was at that moment. I contemplated calling out, inviting him to join us, but something stopped me. This was no ordinary man. Whether it was his walk, or the way he peered up at the hotel, I knew better than to shout to him. I felt in my gut that he would be as crazed as Walter or Alice. If he got close enough, I would see that same slack jawed expression, the same lust for violence, in his eyes.

I gripped the gun tightly and waited, wondering what would

happen next. Was he the only one? Were there more of them beyond the parking lot, traveling along the road, wandering aimlessly? I ran some mental math in my head, figuring out how long it would take to get back and alert the others should the crazy out on the road make a move in our direction. My idea to walk the balcony now felt foolhardy. Thankfully, before long the crazie turned away and resumed his shambolic walk along the road, and soon he was gone.

I waited a while longer, keeping my eyes fixed on the spot where the man had vanished into the night, but the road was quiet now, empty, at least as far as I could see. Relieved, I turned back toward the room, walking faster now. I turned the corner, deciding at the same time not to mention what I had seen. The crazy was gone, so there was no point in scaring the others.

I was pushing the gun back into my belt when Darwin emerged, his eyes red and puffy, as if he'd just woken up. He looked confused for a moment, clearly expecting to see me right there by the door, but he waved when I drew closer.

"Taking a stroll?"

"Something like that," I replied. "Just trying to stay awake." If he noticed the strain in my voice, he said nothing.

"I'll take over from here," Darwin said. "I gotta warn you; Clara snores like you wouldn't believe. I barely got any sleep."

"Thanks, I'll keep that in mind." I suppressed a smile.

"You're welcome." He eyed the gun in my belt. "I should have some protection while I'm out here."

There was no way I was giving him the gun. The last thing we needed was him seeing some crazy walking along out on the road and taking a pot shot at it, alerting it to our presence. I nodded toward the crowbar, which was propped against the wall next to the door. "You can use that."

"Really?" He looked disappointed. "Are you sure I shouldn't have something a little less hands on? Seems like I'd have to get mighty close to someone to use that thing."

"You'll be fine," I said. "If you see anything, just come and wake me up."

"Well, okay." His eyes lingered on the pistol before he turned away and leaned on the railing, looking down into the parking lot below. "Can I ask you something?"

"What?"

"Can I come with you tomorrow when you leave?" He glanced back at me. "I don't want to stay here anymore, and I heard the girls talking about going to New Haven."

"Sure." I had figured he would want to come with us. "You are going to have to leave the pot behind though."

"Really?" He raised his eyebrows. "All of it?"

"All of it. We'll need you to be alert. It's not safe out there."

"Like it's been safe here?"

"That's the deal, take it or leave it."

"Fine." He turned back to the parking lot, sullen.

I waited a moment, expecting him to say something else, but he didn't, so I made my way back to the room and climbed into bed, the weird apparition heavy on my mind.

CHAPTER THIRTY-THREE

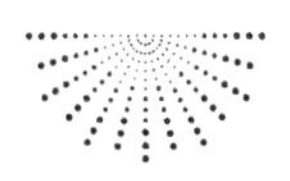

SOMEONE WAS SHAKING ME. I opened my eyes, blinked away the sleep, and tried to focus. Weak light filtered through the red and yellow striped drapes, finding its way in through the gap between the curtains. I sat up. "What is it?"

"There's something going on outside." Darwin's eyes were wide with fear. "You have to see this."

From the other bed, I heard Emily and Clara stir.

"What is it?" Clara asked. "Has Alice come back?"

"Sort of," Darwin said, enigmatic. "Only much worse."

"Oh great," Emily said. "She was bad enough. What do you call much worse?"

"Just come and see. It's freaking strange." Darwin practically pulled me out of bed. He was hopping from foot to foot, as if the floor were a bed of live coals. "Hurry."

"Alright. Easy there." I stood and reached for my pants, pulling them up over my boxers, then slipped into my shoes. I turned to the girls. "Get dressed, and move the backpacks to the door. We may need to make a quick escape."

"Okay," Clara said.

"I'll meet you out there." The evening before, we'd taken the time to stuff as much of the food and other supplies as we could into our packs. Now I was glad we had. "Grab some blankets from the beds too, anything you can fit. We may need them."

"Got it." Clara nodded.

"And don't take too long."

"Come on." Darwin was at the door already, glancing outside, nervous. "Bring the gun too."

"Right." I exchanged a glance with Clara, then pushed the pistol back into my belt and followed the desk clerk outside.

What I saw stopped me dead in my tracks.

The road was full of crazies.

There must have been fifty in all shapes and sizes, old and young, male and female. I spotted a man who must have been pushing eighty years old, and a kid no older than six. One guy wore a cop's uniform. Some people must have been sleeping or preparing for bed when the virus affected them, given their partial state of undress, ranging from nothing at all in one case to underwear or bedclothes. They shuffled, moving slowly, their heads turned in our direction, although they were not coming any closer. I wondered if the man I'd seen the night before was among them, but it was impossible to tell since I'd not gotten a good look at him. I recognized one person, though.

In the middle of the group, standing stock still, I spied Alice in her bloody uniform, her arm still hanging limp and broken to her side.

"This is not good." I pulled the pistol from my belt. "How long have they been here?"

"They appeared a few minutes before I woke you," Darwin said. "Alice showed up first. I didn't want to disturb anyone, so I went for a pee around the corner. When I came back she was standing there, just like she is now."

"And the others?" I asked, as Clara and Emily came up behind me.

"They arrived pretty quickly," Darwin said. "They were

attracted to her somehow. Some came off the interstate, others from the fields. It was freaking creepy."

"Why aren't they moving?" asked Clara.

"I dunno. They stopped right there. Not a one of them has set foot into the parking lot so far. They're staying in the road as if there's an invisible barrier." He scratched his head. "They know we're here. Alice looked right at me."

Emily watched the crazies with a look of revulsion on her face. "I don't want to be here anymore."

"We'll leave soon enough." I assured her. "First, we need to figure out what they are up to. I don't like it."

"Me either." The crowbar had found its way into Clara's hands again. "They should be trying to get up here and kill us."

"Maybe they're getting better," Darwin said hopefully. "I mean, if it is a virus they could fight it off, right, like a cold?"

"I don't think it works that way," I said. "Besides, they don't look any saner than the other ones we've encountered. They are just not attacking us right now."

"Alice seems to be as crazy as she was yesterday," Clara chipped in. "She gives me the creeps, standing there like that."

"It's almost as if they sense something," Emily said. "Maybe they're afraid."

I turned to her, surprised. "Of what?"

"I don't know, but they say dogs can feel things we can't, vibrations, high-frequency sounds," she explained. "Some people believe they can even see ghosts. Maybe the crazies sense things too."

"Well, for one, they're human, not dogs, so it's unlikely they have suddenly developed some sort of sixth sense," I countered. "Besides, what could they possibly be afraid of?"

"I think I know," Clara whispered. Her eyes had strayed from the road and the crazies to the roofline of the motel across the parking lot. Her face was white. "Look."

I glanced up and suddenly understood why the crazies

wanted nothing to do with us. Creeping silently along the roofline were several creatures, their skin dark and oily. They moved forward on all fours, powerful muscles rippling. As they walked, their bony, muscular heads moved from side to side, coal-black eyes inset under deep boned brows. Rows of vicious pointed teeth extended up and down from powerful oversized jaws, the canine teeth at the corners of the mouth so long they looked like daggers.

Emily stifled a shriek.

"Oh, sweet Jesus. What are those things?" Darwin back peddled, nearly bumping into me.

I reached out and grabbed him, realizing that he was about to turn tail and run. "Keep calm. Whatever those things are, we don't want to draw their attention."

"They don't look like any animal I've ever seen."

"No, they don't."

"Maybe they escaped from a zoo," Emily said. Her voice cracked when she spoke.

"I don't think so." I watched the closest creature slink along the roof, hunkered down. When it turned in our direction, I froze. My heart pounded in my chest so loud I thought there was no way we would remain undiscovered, but the beast turned away again, focusing its attention on the crazies.

"This is so not good. Not good." Darwin was visibly shaking. He looked down at the gun. "Why aren't you using that thing? Shoot them."

"Be quiet," I hissed. "I don't think they know we're here yet."

"And I would like to keep it that way," Clara added.

The creatures reached the edge of the roof and stopped. Below them, in the road, the crazies made no move to retreat.

"Put the backpacks on," I said, keeping my voice low, lest I alert the creeping monsters of our presence. "It's time for us to get the hell out of here."

"No shit." Clara hoisted her pack on to her shoulders and handed another to Emily, who did the same.

"Darwin, if we take the stairs, can we skirt to the back of the hotel?" I was in no hurry to tangle with the crazies or the things on the roof.

"Yes. There's another parking lot back there, then a fence, but it's rotten. It should be pretty easy to get through. There's nothing but trees after that."

"We'll need to move the stuff we blocked the stairs with," Clara said, her eyes still rooted on the creatures.

"I know." The same thought had occurred to me, and I was not sure how we were going to achieve that without alerting the roof monsters that we were there, especially since I was fairly sure there were more of them above us on our side of the building. Regardless, one thing was evident; if we waited, we would likely end up worse off than if we moved. "We'll deal with that when we get to it. Maybe we can climb over."

I slipped my backpack over one shoulder and motioned the others to start along the corridor, but before anyone took a step, the creatures lifted their heads high, let out an almighty screech, and leapt forward.

CHAPTER THIRTY-FOUR

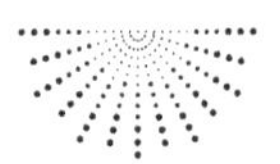

THE CREATURES CATAPULTED themselves from the roof, dropping two floors and landing upright on their feet as if it were nothing at all. They padded forward, slow and deliberate. A couple of them broke away and circled behind their prey, blocking the only avenue of escape.

Now the crazies became agitated, realizing their predicament. They jostled and pushed each other in their haste to retreat, but there was nowhere to go.

For a moment, time stood still. The monsters and crazies faced each other, a hushed silence falling upon the scene. Even the breeze subsided, dying down to nothing.

And then, as one, the creatures leapt, as if responding to some imperceptible cue. They landed among the crazies in a fit of snarling and biting and snapping.

I stood temporarily transfixed, my eyes riveted to the bloodbath unfolding before me. The creatures tore into the crazies until the ground was slick and red, and body parts fell like rain. Here was an arm, there part of a leg. I wanted to look away, to run and never stop, but like a gawker at a traffic accident I was hooked, at least until I felt a gentle tug on my arm.

"We have to get out of here." It was Clara speaking, her face twisted with fear and loathing. "Before they turn on us."

The spell was broken.

"Let's go." I pulled the pistol from my belt, released the safety, and racked the gun.

We made our way along the corridor, keeping as close to the inner wall as we could lest we draw any unwanted attention. Behind us the melee continued, the creatures snarling and growling, the crazies grunting as they were cut down. Although I could not see the action anymore, it took little to imagine who was winning the fight. Soon, the creatures would finish up with their meal of formerly human nut jobs and come looking for fresh meat. I had no intention of being that meat.

We reached the stairwell and could go no further. Our path was blocked with dressers and box springs dragged from nearby hotel rooms and piled there the previous evening. As one, we set our sights on clearing the way, now heedless of making too much noise given the racket coming from the direction of the road.

We dragged the heavier items, the dressers, out of the way. The lighter stuff, such as box springs and nightstands, we either heaved to one side or pushed forward until they lost their balance and toppled down the steps. Soon, we had a clear passage through the mess, enabling us to make our escape. We tackled the stairs at such a clip that we risked falling, but none of us had any intention of slowing down. The faster we went, the quicker we removed ourselves from the vicinity of the creatures.

Upon reaching the ground floor, we sprinted toward the fence, our feet pounding the pavement, drumming in syncopated rhythm, as we ran. Had we been a little more cautious, rather than focusing our attention solely on reaching the fence and the comparative safety of the woods, we might have seen the danger skulking near the dumpsters. As it was, we didn't take notice until it was too late.

CHAPTER THIRTY-FIVE

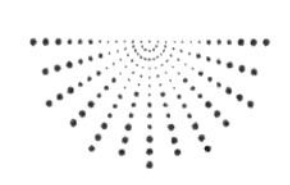

THE CREATURE HIT CLARA MIDSECTION, and together they tumbled to the ground, rolling over and over before coming to rest with Clara on the bottom.

"Shit." I skidded to a halt and turned in time to see the beast rear up, ready for the kill. For a moment I froze, paralyzed. Then I remembered the pistol. I raised it and aimed, squeezing the trigger. The gun bucked, sending a jolt of pain up my arm.

The bullet missed by a mile.

Instead of hitting the target, it whizzed harmlessly right of the mark and thudded into the fence beyond.

Clara screamed, thrusting the crowbar upward to deflect the descending jaws of the beast. It bit down on the metal rod and shook, ripping the weapon from her hands, then tossed it aside with a flick of its head. The crowbar clattered to the ground, useless, out of reach.

I fired again.

This time the bullet smacked home, burying itself into the muscular flesh of the beast's shoulder. It let out a high-pitched squeal full of pain and anger, then swiveled toward me, releasing Clara as it did so. She scuttled backward, grabbing the crowbar lest the creature turn its attention to her once again.

It didn't.

Its attention was fully on me now. It took a step forward, then another, flexing the huge talons on its front paws as if warming them up for the kill it surely expected. Brown saliva oozed from between large boned, heavy jaws as it lowered itself and tensed on bulging back legs, ready to attack.

Then it leapt forward.

I fired wildly in the direction of the fast approaching creature until the gun clicked empty, scoring a direct hit by pure luck. A single bullet smashed into the beast's exposed underside, twisting it in mid-flight. It crashed to the ground and slid for a moment before coming to rest in a heap several feet away.

"Are you alright?" I asked Clara.

She was on her feet now, a trickle of blood running down her face from an inch long gash above her left eye. She lifted her hand to the wound and winced. "Could be better, but I'll live."

"Is that thing dead?" Darwin was wide eyed, his face ashen.

"I have no idea."

"It's bleeding," Emily said. "And the blood is black."

A pool of thick black liquid oozed from the bullet hole, spreading across the ground like an oil spill.

"Come over here." I motioned to Clara.

She hesitated, her attention on the prone beast.

"Come on." I reached out to her. "I don't know if that thing is dead or just stunned. We have to go, now."

She nodded and skirted the creature, keeping well away from the curved claws and ferocious jaws. She ran the last few feet, then threw her arms around me and buried her head in my shoulder, weeping softly.

"Uh, guys?" Emily spoke softly, her gaze focused past me toward the motel. "We have a problem."

I turned as two more creatures rounded the building, their

heads swaying from side to side as if they were following our scent. When they saw us they froze, their gaze moving between the downed beast and us.

I knew their caution wouldn't last long.

"Go. Run for the fence!" I shouted, taking hold of Clara and propelling her forward. "Find a way through."

Darwin grabbed Emily's hand and took flight.

I didn't need to look back to know the beasts were giving chase. The heavy thud of their feet as they ran was indication enough.

Darwin and Emily reached the fence line and took hold of the slats, pulling with all their might. The first came off with ease. They discarded it and went to work on the slats on either side.

I turned to face the approaching beasts. They had slowed, splitting up and circling from both sides, keeping low, their bodies stretched out, muscles taut.

"Hurry." I glanced back toward Darwin.

"This one won't budge." He was tugging on the fence.

"Mine's coming loose," Emily said as her slat gave way with a groan. She threw it to the ground and immediately turned to the next. "Removing three should be enough of a hole for us to get through."

"Agreed." I watched the beasts, sensing their intentions a split second before they attacked.

The creatures arched through the air.

Darwin gave up on the fence and swiveled, scooping up a slat from the ground as he did so, then brought it to bear on the closest creature's head. The slat broke, crumpling on the beast's skull in a hail of splinters. The creature's head snapped sideways, and it dropped to the ground, momentarily stunned.

Then he rushed forward, pushing me out of the way and bringing the broken piece of fence up with all his might, impaling the second creature mid-flight. The beast's momentum forced it down further onto the sharp shard of wood as the slat ripped from Darwin's grasp.

The beast crumpled to the earth, tongue lolling from its open jaws, eyes glazed over.

"Done." Emily discarded another slat. "This should be big enough."

"Hurry," I said as three more creatures emerged from the side of the motel, their bulbous heads raised as they sniffed the air for our scent. "When you get through the fence run for the trees, and whatever happens, don't stop."

CHAPTER THIRTY-SIX

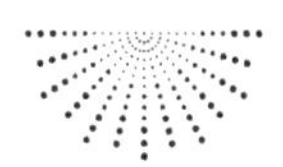

WE RAN FOR A long time, putting as much distance between the creatures and ourselves as possible. I weaved in and out of the trees, pushing deeper into the woods until my legs felt like lead and my lungs screamed for relief. Eventually, able to run no more, I collapsed against a tree trunk, wheezing like an eighty-year-old asthmatic.

Clara flopped down next to me. "Do you think we're safe?"

"I don't think they followed us." We were deep in the woods, and I had heard no sounds of pursuit. I turned to Darwin. "That was pretty brave, what you did back there."

"Yeah." He grimaced, gripping his left side. Blood oozed between his fingers. "I think one of them got me though."

"Let me see." Emily pushed past us and pulled his hand aside to reveal a deep gash, the skin sliced clean through to the muscle. "Oh man, it's pretty deep."

"I'm fine," Darwin said. His face told a different story.

"It's going to need attention before we can travel any further." She shrugged off her pack and delved into it, bringing out a small red plastic box with a white cross printed on top.

"Where did you get a first aid kit?" Clara asked, her face full of admiration.

"Found it back at the motel, in the office. I thought we might need it, and I was right." Emily opened it up and took out a small bottle of antiseptic. She turned to Darwin. "This is going to hurt a bit."

"Okay." He drew a sharp breath and looked away.

Emily opened the bottle and sprayed a good measure of the liquid on the wound.

Darwin let out a small cry of pain, then gritted his teeth. "Christ, that hurts."

"I told you it would sting a bit."

"Well, you lied. It hurts like the devil."

"Don't be such a baby," Emily chastised him.

I exchanged a glance with Clara, surprised at Emily's sudden take-charge attitude.

"Now what?" Darwin looked down at the open wound, moving his hand to cover it once more.

"Don't do that." She slapped his hand away and shot him a withering look. "We have to close it up and dress it or it will get infected."

"And how are you going to do that?" Darwin looked miffed.

"With this." She delved into her pack a second time and came up with a small sewing kit.

"Oh, hell no." Darwin squirmed out of reach and shook his head. "You're not sticking me with any needles."

"I am too." She looked over at us. "Hold him still, will you?"

"Are you sure about this?" Clara looked worried.

"I'm sure." She rooted through the kit until she found the longest needle and held it up, then took a reel of white cotton thread and twisted the end tight with her fingers before deftly threading the eye.

"Wow. You nailed that the first time." Now Clara looked impressed. "It takes me about fifty tries to thread a needle."

"My mother taught me how to sew when I was a kid," Emily said. "Plus, I got lucky."

"Can't we wait until we find a doctor?" Darwin looked like he was about to throw up.

"Absolutely. I'm sure there's a doctor here somewhere." She motioned to us. "Keep him still. If he struggles, I'm likely to stab him instead of fixing him."

"Got it." I took a step forward.

"Alright, alright. I'll keep still and let her mutilate me." Darwin waved me off. "You don't need to hold me."

"Good, now stop moving." Emily took the wound and pinched it together.

"Ow! That hurt," Darwin exclaimed.

"Yeah, well this is going to hurt a lot more before it gets better." She pushed the needle through the clenched skin until it poked out the other side and then pulled it all the way, tugging tightly. Looping the thread, she repeated the procedure, eliciting another whimper from her patient.

"Aren't you done yet?" Darwin looked miserable. He clenched his fists as she made a third pass.

"Almost there; just a couple more."

"Well, hurry."

"Stop rushing me." She pushed the needle through once more, and then looped the end in a knot, tying under and over. Finally, she took a small pair of scissors from the first aid kit and snipped the thread. "How's that feel?"

"Done?" Darwin asked, hopeful.

"Done." She picked a large self-adhesive bandage patch, ripped off the wrappings, and applied it to the sutured wound. "There. I think you'll live."

"Thanks for the hearty prognosis." Darwin touched the bandaged area gingerly. "It feels funny."

"Leave it alone." Emily packed everything away and slipped it back into her pack. "I'll dress it again the next time we stop."

"How did you learn to do that?" I asked.

"I took a year of pre-med before switching majors. I liked the idea of being a medical student more than the practice." She shouldered her backpack. "At least it finally came in useful."

"I'll say."

"We've been here too long," Clara said. "We can't take a chance that those things back at the motel followed us."

"Agreed." There was no sign that the creatures had given chase once we entered the woods, but I didn't like the idea of being caught in such a confined area. Plus, the beasts were clearly adept at climbing since they were on the roof of the motel, which meant they could be above us in the branches.

"Which way?" Emily looked around. "It all looks the same."

"I think we came from that direction. It looks kind of familiar." Now that I thought about it, I didn't know from which direction we had come. We had been running blindly, and I took little notice of landmarks or the scenery.

"Well, nothing looks familiar to me," Clara said.

"Me either." Darwin shook his head.

"Great. We're lost." Emily leaned against a tree. "Now what do we do?"

"I guess we pick a direction and hope it doesn't lead us back to the motel."

"What about the sun?" Darwin suddenly looked hopeful.

"What about it?" I said.

"Well, it sets in the west, right?"

"So what?" I wasn't sure where he was going with this.

"So, the sun always sets over the highway in front of the hotel. The sunlight coming in through the windows almost blinds me in the late afternoon when I'm at the front desk. That means that if we were running away from the motel, out the back, then we were running east."

"So all we have to do is see where the sun is."

"Exactly."

As one, we looked up past the canopy of trees toward the sky, but there was no sun. Instead, all we found were angry black storm clouds.

CHAPTER THIRTY-SEVEN

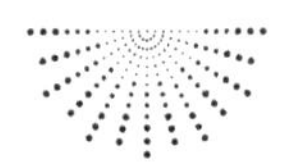

THE STORM BROKE a few minutes after we resumed walking. Huge drops of rain the size of grapes pounded the trees and drenched the earth. The forest canopy gave us some protection, but not much. Mostly it collected the water until there was a critical mass and then dumped it on us in a sheet of icy cold wet misery.

Lacking any means to take our bearings, we made our best guess regarding which direction to go in. I wasn't sure if we were heading away from, or toward the motel, and the awful creatures that now inhabited it. We were left with little choice but to press on.

"This sucks," Darwin moaned. "I wish I'd brought a coat."

"We all do." A rumble of thunder growled overhead, deep and ominous.

"We're going to catch our death out here," Emily said, hugging her arms to her body in a futile attempt to keep out the rain. "The temperature is dropping too."

"I noticed that." It had gone from what felt like the mid-seventies, a fairly normal summer day in Vermont, to bone chillingly cold in the space of thirty minutes. I was no meteorologist, but it felt like too much of a drop, even in a storm.

"I think the rain is getting worse," Clara said, bending her head low as she walked to avoid the worst of the moisture.

"At least it will be harder for those creatures to track us." I stumbled forward, dragging my feet up with every step, my shoes mired in the mud. "I can't imagine they will be able to follow our scent in this."

"They can follow our footprints instead," Emily replied, pulling her own foot out of the muck.

"I'm trying not to think about that," I said. "What I'm more worried about right now is finding some shelter until this thing passes. I'm not sure we're safe out here."

As if to punctuate my observation, a mighty crack of lightning lit up the sky, followed by a boom and the sound of splintering wood.

"Christ, that was close!" Darwin exclaimed.

"It must have hit a tree," Clara said. "The storm is right over us."

"I hate lightening." Emily looked worried.

"It's fine. The chances of being hit are one in a million." I soothed her. "Besides, there are plenty of trees above us and lightning always goes to the highest conductor."

"Is that right?" Emily asked, her face relaxing a little.

"Actually, no," Darwin said. "Given a lifespan of at least eighty years, the chance of being struck by lighting is about one in twelve thousand."

"That's much worse." The panic was back on Emily's face.

"Good going, slick." I glared at Darwin. "I guess tact is not your strong suit."

"How do you even know that?" Clara asked.

"Discovery Channel."

Another flash lit up the sky, followed by a second crash as the lightning touched down.

"That was much closer." Now Clara looked concerned.

"Don't worry about it. We just need to keep on moving." I was drenched, the rain soaking my clothes, which stuck to me with every step. My sodden shoes, now half filled with mud, made walking a misery.

"Easy for you to say," Emily replied. "You don't have a–" She never finished the sentence.

Without warning, a blinding spear of electricity split the air. It slammed into a nearby tree, sending charred splinters flying in all directions.

"Holy crap." Darwin swiveled away from the blast, stepping in front of Emily to protect her from debris.

I pushed Clara forward as a large branch crashed down between us, thumping into the soft earth and sending a spray of mud into the air.

"What in hell?" Clara looked down at the branch, visibly shaken. After a moment of reflection, she glanced up at me. "If you hadn't pushed me out of the way, I would be dead."

"Look, the tree is on fire," Emily said, pointing.

"Why does it seem like everything is out to kill us?" I grumbled. The tree was engulfed in flames despite the downpour. Fire licked at the trunk, which was ripped into two halves by the bolt as if a meat cleaver had separated it. An odor of ozone and soot hung in the air.

"That was too close," Emily said.

Another crackle of lightning flashed across the sky, followed by a rumbling roar of thunder. Somewhere out in the woods came a ripping, rending sound as the powerful bolt went to ground.

"I think that was another tree." Clara stepped close to me. Her clothes were so wet they clung to her, highlighting every curve. "I've never seen a storm like this."

"Me neither." I put my arm around her, feeling her shiver as I did so. "Let's push on. We have to find shelter."

I took a step forward, but before I could take a second one the sky erupted in a deadly light show, streaks of electricity fanning out in all directions at once, then arcing down, smashing through the trees in a cacophony of bursting wood, swiftly followed by a rumble so loud it felt like my eardrums would implode.

CHAPTER THIRTY-EIGHT

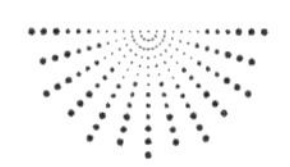

"THIS WAY." I PULLED Clara forward as the world collapsed around us. We ran through an onslaught of branches and fire, lightning bolts smacking into the earth one after the other without even the time to tell where one ended and the next began.

It was chaos.

I dodged a falling tree trunk, skidding sideways to avoid being crushed. Behind me, I could hear the others as they followed, each new explosion eliciting a shriek of fear from Emily and a curse from Darwin.

"Look out!" screamed Clara as the air buzzed with a fork of lightning that hit so close I could feel my hair stand up.

Then the hail came. Golf ball sized chunks of ice that punched into the ground, leaving wet, muddy holes. They ripped branches, tore through the canopy and devastated the forest floor. One hailstone caught me on the shoulder, sending a wave of pain flaring up my arm. I grunted and pressed on, all too aware of the cries of pain as the frozen balls of water bombarded my companions. Only what was left of the woods afforded us any protection at all.

An absurd thought came to me; a verse dredged up from Sunday school years before.

The first angel sounded, and there followed hail and fire mingled with blood, and they were cast upon the earth.

The verse from Revelation had been ridiculous to me back then, old dusty words written by people trying to make sense of things they didn't understand and could not comprehend. But at this moment, right now, we were living that very event.

"It's no good!" Darwin caught up with me and shouted the words over the roar of thunder. "We're never going to make it out of this."

"Don't stop. No matter what happens, don't stop." A tree fell somewhere to my left with a creaking, cracking moan. All around us, fires raged, consuming the woodlands.

Then, as if we passed through some invisible curtain, we emerged from the devastation and destruction and found ourselves back in quiet normality.

I pulled up short and stopped, bewildered. I could still see the fires raging in the woods, still hear the thunder and the cracks as lightning tore through the trees. But here, in this one spot, we were safe. A hailstone bounced and hit the ground, rolling toward us and coming to rest in a bright patch of unlikely sun.

"Oh, thank God." Clara leaned over, catching her breath. "We outran it."

"I'm not sure that we did outrun it. I think it just stopped." I looked up past the trees, at the ragged wall of angry black clouds stretching upward toward the heavens, and the expanse of deep blue sky that stretched away from it.

"It's like the storm can't come any closer," Emily said, her eyes fixed on the odd spectacle of the forest burning, the rain still falling, only yards away from us. She voiced what we were all thinking. "Weird."

"Reminds me of Florida. One minute it's raining, the next you drive out of it into dry sunshine," Clara said. "Only so much worse. I've never seen a storm this violent."

"Well, I for one don't care how weird it is," Darwin replied. "I'm just happy that nothing is trying to kill us, at least for a few minutes."

CHAPTER THIRTY-NINE

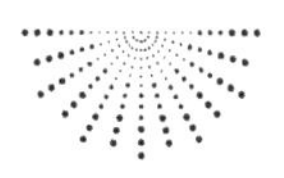

WE PRESSED ON through the woods, which by now felt never ending. After a while, the terrain took a sharp turn upward, and the going got tougher, especially since we were all dog-tired and physically battered. The strange storm, which had come out of nowhere and ended just as abruptly, did not advance toward us. Soon the rumbling thunder and sharp booms as lightning touched down became ever more distant, until we could no longer hear them at all.

Finally, deciding it was safer to stop than to keep pressing forward in our wet and weakened condition, we came across a small glade surrounded by dense undergrowth and tall trees. I made a suggestion to the group. "We should stop here until morning."

"The sun is going down." Clara glanced up at the sky, which had taken on dusky, pastel blue tones, a sure sign of the approaching evening as the sun dipped low in the sky. "Plus, I'm not sure I can walk for much longer. I have a blister on my foot that feels like walking over needles every time I take a step."

"Are you sure we should stop?" Emily looked concerned. "We'll be awfully vulnerable out in the open like this."

"I haven't seen a road or a building since we left the motel," I told her. "The only other choice is to keep walking, and pretty soon it will get dark and that will be impossible."

"I wish we had a tent." Darwin dropped his pack on the ground and sat down. He pulled his shoes off and rubbed his feet. "Or at least a sleeping bag."

"We can clear some space on the ground and pile leaves up, so it's not so hard."

"And we have blankets," Clara said. "I stuffed a couple into the packs."

"Good." I shrugged my pack from my shoulders. "It's agreed then. We stay here tonight and press on in the morning. First order of business, let's build a fire."

"Are you sure about that?" Darwin stopped rubbing his feet and looked up at me. "If there are more crazies out there, or worse, if any of those monster things are roaming the area, we might draw them to us."

"Well, if there are crazies close enough to see the fire, they will find us anyway. Most animals are afraid of fire; they stay away from it, so that should take care of those creatures. Besides, I don't particularly want to spend the night in pitch blackness."

"Plus, I'm freezing," Emily said. "If we don't light a fire, we might all catch our deaths. Getting pneumonia out here would not be good."

"Which leads me to my next suggestion," I said. "We should get out of these wet clothes as soon as possible."

"But not before we have a fire going." Clara looked around. "We should collect wood before it gets too dark to see."

"Good idea." I looked forward to getting warm. "Clara and I will gather the firewood."

"What about us?" Darwin asked.

Before I could reply, Emily spoke up. "I need to look at that wound again and apply more antiseptic."

"Great." Darwin looked glum. "I can't wait."

CHAPTER FORTY

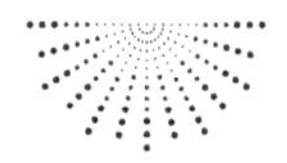

WE GATHERED WOOD in silence for a while, venturing as far from the clearing as we dared, but making sure never to stray too far. We also kept within eye line of each other. The last thing I wanted was to lose anyone, especially Clara.

Incredibly, it didn't seem to have rained at all here. The branches and twigs were bone dry, which came as a relief. If they had been wet, we would have been in trouble. I selected several fat limbs, figuring that they would take longer to burn, and left the smaller stuff for Clara. When we each had an armful, we made our way back to the others, deposited our wood, and went to collect more.

I did not know how much we would need to keep us going through the night, but I knew I had no intention of letting the fire burn out. If we found ourselves under attack, as was happening regularly, we would need to see our attackers. Given the surprises of the last few days, who knew what would come at us next. It wouldn't have surprised me to find a dinosaur charging through the woods at this point.

By the third trip, our pile of wood was fairly large, and I guessed one more would do it. The light was waning fast, and we still had to set up camp and start the fire. We made our way back out, skirting the perimeter of the clearing and picking up what remained of the ground wood. Whatever we had scavenged would have to suffice.

Returning to the makeshift camp, we found that Darwin, his wound freshly dressed, had taken it upon himself to scoop out a hollow of earth and pile it high with wood, kindling and twigs on the bottom, along with handfuls of dried leaves, and the larger chunks on top. The newly created fire pit looked every bit as good as anything I'd ever made during my days in the Boy Scouts. I wondered where Darwin had learned to be so outdoorsy.

"Looks good." I dropped my last armful of wood onto the pile. "We still need to light it though."

"Shit." Clara looked disappointed. "I hadn't thought about that. How are we going to get it going?"

"We could rub two sticks together," Emily said.

"Does that even work?" Clara replied, the skepticism in her voice clear.

"I don't know. It does in the movies."

"No need for that." Darwin looked pleased with himself. He dug his hand into his pocket and pulled out a lighter. "We have this."

"You are full of surprises." Emily beamed from ear to ear.

"Perk of being a pothead." He grinned.

I rubbed my hands on my trousers to clear the dirt and bits of bark away. "So, what are we waiting for? Light it."

CHAPTER FORTY-ONE

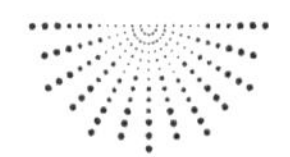

THE FIRE CAST LONG shadows over the clearing, the flames providing some comfort against the onslaught of night. For all I knew, we were drawing crazies to us by the dozen. But I didn't think so, not this far into the woods, and the fire would surely keep away most of the nocturnal wildlife.

I felt like crap. My clothing, soaked through hours ago, was now damp and cold against my skin. My shirt was ruined. Large stains smeared the front of it, and there was a tear below one shoulder where I'd snagged it while pushing through the fence. I peeled the shirt off and discarded it. There was no point in drying it by the fire, since I had no intention of ever wearing it again.

Clara followed suit, stripping off her shirt and unbuckling her pants.

"We're going to undress here?" Emily asked. "Right out in the open?"

"I think circumstances outweigh modesty," Clara said, dropping her pants and kneeling, wearing just her underwear, to find some dry clothes in her pack.

"I agree," I said. It would be a bad idea to split up and change clothes out of sight. We didn't know what was lurking in the woods, if anything, but I didn't want to take any chances. "It's better if we stick together."

"Fine." Emily didn't look happy.

"We can turn our backs." I ventured.

"No. It just feels odd, undressing like this." She pulled her tee up and off. "I mean, I didn't know any of you a few days ago. I don't even like undressing in front of my boyfriend." She paused a moment, then spoke again. "Still, after what we've been through together, it feels like I've known you forever."

"You have a boyfriend?" Darwin glanced sideways at her.

"Used to. We broke up a few weeks back," she said. "He found our relationship too restrictive, said he wanted different things."

"What did he want?" Darwin found a clean shirt, pilfered from one of the guest rooms, and put it on.

"Mainly, he wanted Amy Clements. The bastard." She slid out of her jeans and draped them over a nearby branch to dry, then pulled on a fresh pair. "Funny, he's probably dead now, or crazy. I should feel sad about that, but I don't."

CHAPTER FORTY-TWO

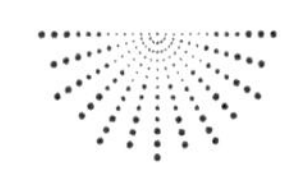

WE SAT AROUND THE FIRE, eating cold baked beans out of cans with the lids pulled back and soaking up the juice with sliced sandwich bread. It was not an ideal meal, and one I would never have imagined myself eating a few days before, but tonight it tasted like heaven. We could have pushed the cans into the bottom of the fire to heat, poking holes in the top to prevent them from exploding, but we were all so hungry that we skipped that step for the sake of swiftness and got straight to the eating part.

A moment of panic set in when I realized we did not have a can opener, a stupid oversight. Luckily, the beans were pull top, so we dodged a bullet, at least this time.

For the longest time nobody said a word, the only sound that of us devouring the oddly satisfying meal and the soft crackling of the wood as it burned. After a while, with our bellies full, we dissected the events of the past few days.

"What do you think they are?" Clara asked.

"What?" I shoveled a spoonful of beans into my mouth, scraping the bottom of the can.

"Those things back at the motel," she said. "Those vile creatures that attacked the crazies, that came after us."

"I don't know." It was the truth. I had never heard of any beast matching the description of the ones we encountered.

Darwin spoke up. "Maybe they escaped from a government lab." He leaned forward, resting his elbows on his knees. "You know, mutants or something."

"I hardly think so," I replied. "Is there even a government facility anywhere near here? Besides, that doesn't explain the crazies. It all has to be linked somehow."

"Have you got a better explanation then?"

"Not really," I admitted. "But I don't think they are mutants."

"Well, they sure as hell aren't pussy cats." Emily picked up a stick and stoked the fire, sending a ribbon of flames leaping into the air.

"My money is on aliens," Darwin said.

"Oh, come on. Really?" That was pushing things too far. I took another piece of bread and bit into it.

"Why not aliens?" Emily countered, leaping to his defense. "There are plenty of theories that extraterrestrial life has visited Earth. The History Channel is full of that stuff."

"Well, they will have a field day now," I muttered. "Assuming things ever get back to normal."

"I think aliens are a long shot," Clara said. "But they must have come from somewhere."

"They didn't seem to like the crazies, that's for sure."

"They didn't like us either." I pointed out. "And the feeling is mutual."

"So that brings us back to the big question," Clara said. "Where did they come from and why?"

"A zoo?" Darwin waggled his spoon. "They looked a bit like panthers."

"Yeah. Panthers with really enormous jaws, and teeth that would make a sabre-toothed cat cry," I retorted.

"And let's not forget those muscles. If they were panthers, they were on steroids," Clara said.

"Right. I think we can safely rule out escapees from a zoo, and while we're at it, lab mutants and aliens too." Now that the crackpot theories were out of the way, I hoped we might have a reasonable discussion regarding the origins of the beasts. I was out of luck.

"What about another dimension?" Darwin came up with one wacky idea after another. "Scientists have theorized that we may live in one of millions of dimensions, all existing in the same space but on separate frequencies."

"This is pointless." I slammed the empty bean can down on the ground and stood up, glaring at Darwin. "What is wrong with you? You're hiding behind stupid theories. Don't you get it? Don't you see what's happening all around us? The entire world has gone to crap. People who were perfectly sane three days ago have turned into mindless killers. Monsters that look like something out of a horror movie are stalking us, and not even the weather is acting right."

"Hey, he's just trying to make sense of things." Clara reached out and put her hand on my arm. "We all are."

"I know." I sat back down and took a deep breath. It wasn't Darwin's fault, but there was steam I needed to vent, and he was the easiest target. "Sorry." I cast him a sideways glance.

"Well-" He looked hurt.

"Come on... I didn't mean anything by it."

"Fine."

"Great," Clara said. "Can we play nice from now on, boys?"

I nodded.

"That's better." She rummaged in a bag and took out a soda, popping the top and drinking before speaking again. "Let's all agree that it's not aliens or mutants, shall we?"

Now Darwin nodded.

"I'm sure there's a rational explanation for all this."

"Like what?" Darwin asked.

"It has to be a virus that turned everyone into crazies. It's the only thing that makes any sense."

"Fine, but that still doesn't explain the panthers." Great. Now I was thinking of them as big cats, which we all knew they were not. "Even if we assume the humans fell victim to a virus of some sort, we are still left with the puzzle of those creatures. There's nothing the right shape or size for an animal like that living in North America, let alone here."

"There have been sightings of cougars and mountain lions in recent years." Darwin spoke softly, testing the waters to see if I would go off on him again. "They are scarce, but they would be about the right size."

"I don't see it. Those things looked nothing like a big cat. They looked-" I searched for the right word.

"Monstrous." Clara filled in the blank.

"Thank you. Monstrous." That was an appropriate word. "Besides, what type of virus would make people go mad, then jump species and turn big cats into monsters like that? I mean, it would have to be a physical change, not just a mental one. I'm no biologist, but I don't think it's even possible for an infection to do that kind of thing."

"If only we had access to the internet," Emily said. "I bet we could find out what was going on then."

"Oh yes, Wikipedia knows all," I muttered.

"Sorry?"

"I am agreeing with you."

"There is something else too." Clara reached out and warmed her hands by the fire. "All the missing people."

"We don't know for sure that they are missing. Maybe they all went off reservation, went nuts." My thoughts returned to the woman with the BMW back at the gas station. If she had turned crazy, we would surely have encountered her when we ran across Walter. Then again, Walter could have gotten to her too. That didn't explain the other odd instances where there should have been people or bodies.

As if reading my mind, Clara asked, "What about the cars on the highway? You said yourself that the seatbelts were still buckled, the doors jammed. Those people couldn't have escaped. Same with the pilots in the downed plane. And Emily said that she was alone when she woke up in the school library. There should have been many more people at the school than there was."

"I know, I know. I don't have an answer." I wished I did. Something else nagged at me too; how we'd all blacked out at the same time. I was about to mention that, but suddenly my phone vibrated.

I had received another text.

CHAPTER FORTY-THREE

FOR THE LONGEST TIME, no one spoke.

We huddled around the phone and stared at the screen, at the text message sitting there in all its back-lit glory.

VIRUS UNSTABLE
NORTH NOT SAFE
GO TO NEW HAVEN

"What does that mean," Clara asked, finally breaking the silence. "North not safe?"

"Beats me. It doesn't sound good," I said. I read the text again, but it didn't get any better the second time.

"I don't like the part about the virus," Emily said. "It sounds like it's spreading. What if one of us comes down with it?"

"I guess if that happens, we deal with it then. Thinking about the possibility will do no good; it will only make us feel paranoid and scared," Clara said. "We stick together, we continue to head south, and we'll be fine."

"Is it from your brother, like the last time?" Emily asked.

"It's his number for sure. Other than that, I don't know."

"How can your phone have any battery power left?" Emily asked. "You haven't charged it. There has been no power since the first afternoon."

"Another good question." I was as baffled as everyone else, especially since the phone still showed twenty-five percent juice. "I'd like to say it has awesome battery life, but there's no way it should still work now."

"Finally some contact with the outside world." Darwin looked hopeful. "Call him back."

"It won't work," Clara told him. "We tried last time."

"Last time?" Darwin echoed. "You mean you've been talking to someone all this time?"

"No." I punched the number and hit the option for callback, then put it on speaker. After one ring, an all too familiar voice came on the line. Not my brother, but the same automated message as before. "See? It won't connect. The text messages come in, but I can't send anything out. It's a one-way street, so no conversation."

"That's a shame." Darwin looked crestfallen.

"Yeah, it is." I understood his disappointment. It was nothing compared to my dismay upon discovering that I could not communicate with my brother. In the three days since the world had collapsed, my thoughts had turned to Jeff often. I wondered if the texts really were from him. If they were, what was he doing in New Haven? How had he found his way there? I would have given anything to hear his voice, to know he was really, truly safe. The text messages provided a ray of hope, something to grasp onto. Who else would send messages to me other than Jeff? It had to be him.

"I wish I'd heard from my family," Emily said. "I would give anything to know they are safe."

"Best not to think about it," said Clara.

I glanced at her, remembering her pragmatic decision not to bother trying to reach her parents in Florida. I wished I could say something that would make her feel better, but what was there to say?

"Makes me glad I never knew my parents," Darwin said. "Makes things easier."

"You never knew your parents?" A look of sadness crossed Emily's face. "Why?"

"I don't know. I grew up in foster homes." He looked down into his can of beans. "I spent most of my childhood bouncing from place to place until I reached eighteen and then I was on my own."

"That's awful." Emily looked shocked. "I'm so sorry."

"It's okay." He smiled. "Turned out to be a good thing in the end. I'm the only one not worried about anyone else."

Emily shot a look at him.

"Except you guys, of course," he said. "I'm glad you were there when those beasts came. I don't know what I would have done on my own. I'd be a half digested meal for one of them by now."

"And it would be high as a kite," I said. "Judging by the amount of pot you had."

There was a moment of silence, and then everyone burst out laughing.

CHAPTER FORTY-FOUR

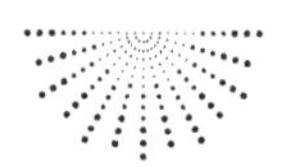

WE TURNED IN AT AROUND midnight, the text message still weighing heavy on my mind. I wanted to believe it was from Jeff. I didn't want to think about the contents of the message. Was the storm we had passed through what he was talking about when he said the north was not safe? I also wondered about the crazies. Was the virus referencing them, the strange beasts at the motel, or did it allude to some other, more frightening thing we had yet to discover?

We only had two blankets, which meant that the girls shared one, and Darwin and I split the other one. Since we didn't feel safe with everyone sleeping at once, we took turns keeping watch as we had done the previous evening.

With one exception.

Clara and Emily both insisted on taking turns. They had been spared guard duty the night before and said it wasn't fair to burden Darwin and me again. Not looking forward to another sleepless night, I agreed.

Clara took the first shift. She sat down in front of the fire, throwing another log on and stoking it with a long stick until the flames lit the clearing in a comforting orange glow. Darwin would be next up, followed by Emily, and finally, I would take my turn until dawn.

It was a good arrangement that afforded each of us at least six hours of sleep, and considering the ordeals we had already been through, we would need that sleep if we were to reach New Haven, which felt as distant as it had two nights before in the barn when the first message arrived.

I settled down to sleep, my mind wandering to Clay. I wondered if he was still walking toward Canada, convinced that it was spared the misfortune that had been wrought on the United States. I hoped the crazies hadn't gotten him. If anyone was equipped to fend them off, it would be him. Of course, now we knew the crazies weren't the only things to be afraid of, and I feared he might not fare so well on his own against a pack of the motel beasts. I pushed the thought from my mind and closed my eyes, a fitful sleep finding me within minutes.

CHAPTER FORTY-FIVE

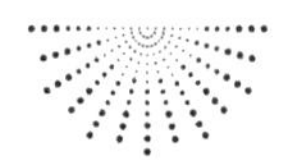

SOMEONE WAS MOVING NEXT to me.

I awoke, groggy and confused.

For a moment, I wondered why my mattress was so hard. Then I remembered I wasn't in my comfortable bed. I was on the floor of a forest in the middle of nowhere, sharing a blanket with a pot smoking desk clerk.

"Darwin," I said. "What are you doing?"

"Hush. Keep your voice down." Came the reply. It didn't sound like Darwin. It sounded like Clara.

What was she doing under the covers with me?

"What's going on," I whispered. "Is everything alright?"

"Everything is fine." I felt a body press against mine, felt Clara's breasts push into my back. "Darwin is keeping watch now. It's his turn."

"Oh." I was confused, but not complaining. "Aren't you supposed to be sharing a blanket with Emily?"

"She looked so peaceful. I didn't have the heart to disturb her," Clara said, snaking an arm around me. "Besides, I feel safer sleeping with you."

"It's going to be awfully cozy in here when Darwin comes

back after his shift," I said. "I'm not sure there will be enough blanket for all three of us."

"Funny," she whispered in my ear.

"I'm just saying."

"I told him to take Emily's blanket when he swaps out with her. It's a win, win situation."

"I see."

"Now shut up," she said. "Go back to sleep."

I felt her breath tickle the back of my neck, warm and pleasant. I wanted to roll over to face her, hold her close and look into her eyes, to kiss her and never let her go ever again. Sleep was the furthest thing from my mind at that moment. It was strange how attached to her I had become in the space of a few short days. She was an attractive girl, but there was something deeper than that. Perhaps our journey, the things we'd been through side by side, drew us closer. I suspected she felt the same way. However, I didn't turn and kiss her. It was not the right time or place. Instead, I said, "Sleep tight, Clara."

CHAPTER FORTY-SIX

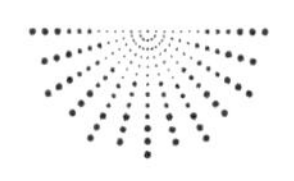

WE SET OUT at first light, continuing on through the forest with no idea where we were. As long as we were heading away from the motel, any direction worked fine for me, especially since I figured we would come across a road at some point and get our bearings, maybe even find our way back to the highway.

After an hour of walking, we came across a stream running through the woods. The pristine, clear water bubbled over rocks and around boulders on its way downhill. Here and there, a large slab of bedrock was exposed, and in these places the water flowed down over the edge in mini waterfalls.

"We should stop here for a moment." I squatted down and let the cool water run over my hand, then scooped some up in my palms and drank before reaching into my pack and pulling out a couple of empty plastic water bottles saved for just such a fortuitous occasion. "We can restock on water."

"Good idea." Clara knelt beside me and filled her own water bottles. "Now if only we could find some food that wasn't baked beans and sandwich bread."

"Really?" I laughed. "A few days ago you were complaining about having nothing to eat but chocolate and chips."

"What I'd really like is a big, fat cheeseburger with extra pickles." She pushed the bottles back into her pack and splashed water on her face. "With a side of fries."

Emily finished filling her own bottle. "Would you quit it? You're making the rest of us hungry now."

"Sorry." Clara grinned.

"Fried chicken." Darwin spoke up. "If I could eat anything in the world right now, it would be fried chicken."

"Fairground fried dough covered in powdered sugar," Emily said. "See, now you've got me at it."

"Movie theater popcorn," I weighed in, "dripping in butter."

"Oh. That sounds so good," Clara agreed. "Not much chance of finding a movie theater around here, I'm afraid."

"That's alright. There aren't any good movies playing anyhow." I joked.

Clara laughed. The sound was music to my ears. "Who cares what the movie is... It's all about the popcorn."

"You are so right. I stand corrected." I stood up and stretched. "Tell you what, if we ever get out of this-"

"Shhh." Darwin waved at me to keep quiet. "Do you hear that?"

"What now?" The sparkle left Clara's eyes, replaced by a look of sheer desperation. "Please tell me we're not going to have to run again. I'm so sick of running away from things."

"Hush." Darwin frowned. "Keep quiet and listen."

For a while no one spoke, each of us straining our ears, listening for whatever Darwin had heard. High above, in the canopy, a bird chirped, eliciting an answering chorus of tweets from somewhere off to our left. The wind rustled the leaves, and the stream made small gurgling sounds as it wound through the landscape. None of this was out of the ordinary.

"I don't hear anything," I said at last.

"I don't hear it now either." Darwin looked perplexed. "Maybe I imagined it."

"We are all exhausted," Clara said. "Lack of sleep can do odd things to a person."

"I'm pretty sure it was real," Darwin said. "Besides, I don't feel all that tired right now."

"What did you think you heard anyway," Emily Asked.

"Music," Darwin replied. "I heard music. It was faint, but definitely there."

"What?" I found it hard to believe anyone would play music in the middle of the woods. Even if there was somebody else out here, which I highly doubted, they would have to be insane to go around playing music, given the circumstances. "Are you sure?"

"Yes." Darwin looked indignant. "Yes, I'm sure. It was Madonna, I think."

"Madonna," I repeated, incredulous. "Is it possible to get flashbacks from too much pot?"

"Hilarious." Darwin stuck his lip out. "I know what I heard. It was Madonna."

"I believe you." Emily put a hand on his shoulder. "What song was it?"

"I didn't hear much of it, just a few snatches," Darwin said, "but I think it was *Like a Virgin,* the old eighties song."

"Well, I'm convinced. How about you?" I turned to Clara, a grin on my face.

"Stop it." Clara punched me playfully on the arm. "You're teasing him."

"Maybe a little." I rubbed my arm in mock distress. "You have quite a left hook there. Let me guess, your father taught you in between showing you how to break in to diners with crowbars."

"Of course. Who else?"

"Shh." This time it was Emily. "Darwin's right. I can hear music."

I glanced at Clara and raised my eyebrows, because now I heard it too. From somewhere out in the woods, drifting on the breeze, came the unmistakable sound of Katrina and the Waves.

CHAPTER FORTY-SEVEN

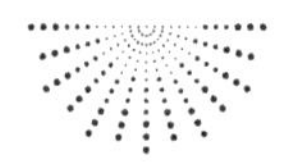

"THAT SOUNDS LIKE *WALKING ON SUNSHINE*." I could not believe my ears. "What the–"

"It is." Clara shook her head. "*Walking on Sunshine*. There must be another survivor out here."

"With a boom box and a bunch of cassette tapes from the eighties, apparently," Emily added. "My mother used to play that song."

"We have to find them." Emily's eyes grew wide. "What if the crazies get to them?"

"I agree." It felt surreal to be listening to pop songs out in the middle of the woods. Did the person playing the music not know that they were in imminent danger, or did they not care? "But let's proceed with caution. Whoever is playing the music might be friendly, but on the other hand, it may be a trap."

"Why would it be a trap?" Darwin said. "What purpose would that serve?"

"Think about it," I said. "What better way to keep us off balance, to get our guard down, than to lure us in thinking we've found someone who doesn't understand what they are doing?"

"Okay, I see where you are coming from. But why would they bother?" Darwin pressed.

"Food, water, guns." I glanced at Clara and Emily. "To get their hands on the girls."

"That's ridiculous," Emily said, but there was a hint of concern on her face even so.

"He's right." Clara put her hands on her hips. Now she sounded nervous. "God knows we've had enough surprises over the last couple of days. I'm with Hayden."

"We find them, but if there's even a hint of danger, we hold back and assess the situation before revealing ourselves." I looked at the group, searching their faces, pleased to see they were all taking my words to heart. "If it looks fishy, we walk away. Agreed?"

"Agreed." As one, the group spoke up.

"So how do we find them?" Emily asked.

"I guess we follow the music." I listened for a moment. The song was winding down, but I thought I could pinpoint the general direction of the sound. "It's this way." I pointed, taking a step toward the waning music, pushing branches aside as I went.

Without hesitation the others followed, first Clara, then Emily, with Darwin bringing up the rear.

We walked in silence until the song ended, then paused, waiting to see if another track would start up. I hoped that whoever was playing the music hadn't decided that enough was enough. The seconds ticked by, one by one, and I thought we might have imagined the music after all. After a pause of maybe half a minute, it started up again, louder now.

We were getting closer.

"Come on," I whispered, getting my bearings once more and pushing forward toward the sound.

After a few minutes, we came to a ravine, a deep trough in the ground that I could see no way around. I started down the slope, slipping a few times on the treacherous leaves that dotted the bank. When I reached the bottom, I turned and reached out, taking Clara's hand and helping her up the last few steps, then waited for the other two before starting up the other side. It was a tough climb, but the music was much louder from here, and I was sure we would come across the source soon.

I wasn't disappointed.

No sooner had I cleared the top of the ravine than I discovered who was playing the music, and why.

And none of it made a lick of sense.

CHAPTER FORTY-EIGHT

"IS THAT WHAT I think it is?" Clara stared in disbelief at the sight that now presented itself.

"I think so." I stood, mouth open like an idiot, staring. "But I'm as baffled as you."

"This is getting too weird," Darwin whispered. "I mean, really screwed up, strange. If I didn't know better, I'd swear you were right, and I was hallucinating."

"Yeah." I blinked, unsure if I was seeing what I thought I was, or if we were all losing our minds.

There, in a wide clearing about fifty feet ahead of us, stood a cluster of small cabins. I counted twelve, arranged in two rows on each side of a central space. Two SUV's and a bright yellow school bus were parked toward the edge of the clearing next to a crudely paved road that snaked away into the woods. But it was the activity in the open space between the rows of cabins that I found so incredible.

A group of people were engaged in what I could only describe as a vigorous aerobics session.

"Are they working out?" Emily asked.

"I think so," I replied. "It certainly looks like they are."

There were at least sixteen people in the clearing, a mix of male and female, all of different ages. They were lined up in two rows, one behind the other, facing a tall man wearing a pair of bright white shorts and a loose fitting tee. He barked out orders to the group, jumping up and down to the beat of the music, his arms swinging wildly as he did so. Even from a distance, I could tell that he was slightly breathless.

"What should we do?" Clara asked. "Do we go on in and introduce ourselves?"

"They look harmless enough," Emily added. "If this is a trap, it gets an A+ from me for originality."

"No shit," Darwin chimed in. "There are easier ways to ambush someone than that. It looks like way too much work. I'm getting out of breath just watching them."

The music ended again. The group stopped exercising and broke ranks, stretching, leaning down with their hands on their knees, catching their breath, or chatting to the person next to them. The ringleader stood with his arms at his side, watching them for a moment, before a new song played and he corralled them all back in line for another frantic session of jumping and jogging on the spot.

"Well? What should we do?" Clara pressed.

"I guess we go in there and say hello." I still felt like we may be walking into something we might regret later, but it seemed far-fetched that this ragtag group of people, bopping out to old songs from thirty years ago, would really be much of a threat. How they had come to be in the middle of the woods in the first place was a mystery, and I really wanted to understand it. Plus, they had cabins, and I was not sure I could take another night sleeping on the forest floor with nothing but a small fire to keep me warm.

"Should we wait for them to finish?" Emily asked. "They look pretty into their workout."

"I don't think so." I stepped from the trees. "Who knows how long that will be."

CHAPTER FORTY-NINE

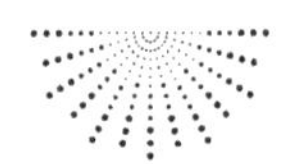

ALL EYES TURNED TOWARD US.

The leader of the group squatted down and shut off a portable CD player, killing the music, before standing again and approaching.

"Can I help you people?" He had a deep bass voice. The kind of voice that made you want to do as he said. "Are you lost?"

"You could say that." I stopped walking and waited for him to close the gap between us. I felt it prudent not to get too close to the group. They looked sane, but on the other hand, they were dancing in a forest clearing. "What is this place?"

"This?" He swept an arm around the clearing like a king surveying his realm. "This is Camp Eden, my little slice of heaven away from the rigors of the real world."

"You're hiding out here?" Emily asked.

"Well, I wouldn't exactly call it hiding. I'm J.T., by the way."

"J.T.?"

"Jonathan Templeton the Third. At your service."

"I know that name!" Darwin exclaimed. "I've heard of you."

I looked at him, confused. "You have?"

"Yes. This is so incredible." Darwin was talking fast, the

words tumbling from his mouth. "You own Endyne Digital Studios."

"Guilty as charged." J.T. looked proud. He puffed his chest out. "But don't hold it against me."

"Are you kidding me? This is freaking awesome." Darwin pumped a fist in the air. Apparently he'd forgotten about the monsters and the crazy people, at least for a moment. "I wish I had my camera with me. What a selfie that would make."

"Okay. Timeout," I said. "Darwin, who is this and how do you know him?"

"I can't believe none of you have heard of this guy." Darwin grinned. "He's a legend."

"Thank you," J.T. interrupted.

Darwin carried on speaking. "Orc Slayer, Dragon Rising, The Halls of Valhalla."

"What are you talking about?" Clara said.

"Video games," Darwin said. "But not just games; the best games ever, and they were all designed by this guy. He's a legend in the gaming universe."

"Well, that explains a few things," I said. It figured that Darwin would be a video game nerd. "But it still doesn't explain all this. Camp Eve or whatever it is."

"Camp Eden," J.T. replied. "My personal, corporate retreat. I come up here several times a year with my brightest and best employees." He grinned.

I wondered if he knew that his teeth looked unnaturally white, much too bright. His deep tan only accentuated the contrast. "So you came up here to escape the attack?"

"We don't know that it was an attack," Clara reminded me. "We don't know what happened."

"Fine," I said. "You came here to get away from the crazies? The beasts?"

"What are you talking about, dear boy?" J.T. looked genuinely confused. "What attack?"

"Four nights ago," I said. "The virus. People going insane, cars refusing to start, cell phones not working. The total collapse of society."

"Oh, this is too good." J.T. grinned, flashing those pearly whites again. "Did Donaldson put you up to this? That old bastard. I knew he would come up with some way to get me back for last year's Christmas party."

"What? No." I stammered. "What are you talking about?"

"Alright, you almost had me, but it's time to drop the act."

"This isn't an act. I'm serious." I pointed back toward the woods, to where we'd emerged. "People are dead. There are burned bodies on the highways, crashed jets, and lunatics trying to kill us. The world has gone to shit."

"Of course it has." J.T. looked puzzled. "A practical joke, right?"

"You don't have a clue, do you?" I realized that J.T. and, by extension, his entire group, actually didn't know what was going on in the outside world. "Don't you guys have cell phones up here? TV? Internet?"

"None of it. This is a retreat. We leave all of that stuff behind and come up here to brainstorm. You know, we remove the distractions."

I looked at him in disbelief. He really, truly didn't know. Behind him, the aerobics class had dispersed and was heading toward the cabins, chatting and laughing among themselves. How was it possible that these people could have been up here all this time, blissfully unaware of the hell being wrought all around them? "Didn't you notice something was wrong when the electricity went out?"

"We have electric," J.T. said. "It works fine."

"That's impossible. Nothing works," Clara protested. "The power is out everywhere."

"Not here," J.T. insisted. "Everything is off the grid. Look." He pointed toward the cabins.

I looked past him, my eyes roaming the clearing, the structures and the vehicles, and then I understood why they hadn't noticed anything amiss, why they were going about their business as if nothing had changed. Every building sported an array of solar panels on its roof, tilted toward the sky. The tree branches that overhung the clearing had been cut back several feet from the cabins to allow the panels to do their job. They probably had well water too, which meant this place was completely self-sufficient. No ties to the outside.

"They have power." Emily looked like she was about to kiss J.T. "Holy crap, they actually have power."

"We do indeed." The look on J.T.'s face had changed from one of bemusement to one of concern. "And now I think you should accompany me to my quarters, and then you can fill me in on what's been going on."

CHAPTER FIFTY

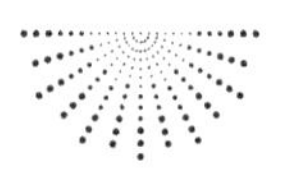

"TELL ME EVERYTHING." J.T. sat opposite us in his sparsely furnished cabin, occupying a high-backed leather swivel chair next to a dark wood desk that contained exactly three items: a lamp, a pen, and a spiral bound notepad.

I took the lead, explaining everything from the headache, my collapse, and finding Clara behind the counter of the gas station, to the motel, and the creatures crawling along the roofline. I told him how we were attacked by Walter, how we came to save Emily, and all about the crazy server locked in the cooler. Through all of this J.T. sat tight-lipped, his fingers arched under his chin, a puzzled look upon his face.

When I finished telling my tale, he remained silent for a moment, his brow furrowed. Finally, as if coming to a mental conclusion, he raised himself from the chair. "Follow me."

He crossed the room to a door in the back of the cabin and drew a key from his pocket. Unlocking it, he invited us through.

The room beyond was a surprise. Unlike the rest of the cabin, which was devoid of all but the most basic items. No TV, no media center, no computer. This room looked like a high-tech playground. Although small, the space contained an array of gadgets. A metal desk, utilitarian in design, occupied one wall. Upon the desk sat a razor thin laptop in sleek aluminum. Mounted on the far wall, there was a large curved TV, sixty inches or more, and beneath that a small cable box with HDMI cords that snaked into the wall. I guessed that somewhere up on the roof, possibly concealed from sight to preserve the ambience of the place, was a satellite dish, although J.T. never confirmed this. It was the object on a small cart near the door that drew my attention. A square, bulky radio base station with a handset clipped to the side.

"I had this room put in for just such an emergency as this. I keep it locked most of the time, only opening it when there's an urgent situation that can't wait until I return to the city. In all the time I've been coming up here, I've needed this place precisely twice. Today will make three," J.T. said. He pulled a metal folding chair out from under the radio cart and sat down. "This is a sideband radio. I've picked up transmissions from Europe on one of these babies before."

"Maybe we can find out if this thing is everywhere, or if it's only the USA," Clara said.

As it had done a few times recently, my mind turned to Clay. If it was just the United States, then it meant he was right all along, and we had made a horrible mistake by not going with him to Canada. At this very moment, he could be sitting in a coffee shop in Montreal, sipping a latte and reading a newspaper. But I had a feeling Clay was not enjoying coffee at a sidewalk café. It was more likely that he was holed up somewhere, or dead by now, especially if he had run into the same vicious creatures we did at the motel.

"Why don't we see what's going on?" J.T. picked up the radio handset and flipped a couple of switches. The unit sprang to life. A dull static hiss filled the air.

"Who are you going to call?" Emily asked.

"Whoever is out there. We are going to bounce the signal off the ionosphere." J.T. toggled the switch on the side of the microphone handset and spoke into it, his words slow and deliberate. "This is Eden Station calling anyone out there. Come back please. Over."

We waited, listening for any sound of a voice coming over the airwaves. All we heard was the hiss of white noise.

"Eden Station calling. If anyone is out there, please respond. Over." J.T. tried again. He lowered the microphone and looked up at us. "We should get a response. Even if the weather conditions were bad, we should at least be able to reach other operators in Canada and Greenland."

"It's useless," Emily said under her breath. "This is a waste of time."

"Maybe," J.T. responded. "But I'll try none-the-less."

He pressed the button again and repeated the message.

We stood in silence around the radio.

Still nothing. Empty static greeted us.

"I don't get it." J.T. placed the handset on its clip and leaned back. "Maybe this thing is broken."

"It's not." I hadn't expected much, but I couldn't help but feel disappointed. "We're not getting a response because there's no one left to answer. The entire world is either dead or crazy."

"Which means we're really on our own," Clara said, her voice trembling. In her face I saw the true gravity of our situation hit home for the very first time.

CHAPTER FIFTY-ONE

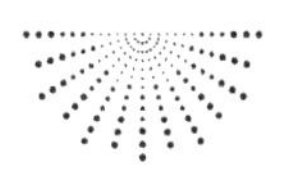

WE SPENT THE rest of the afternoon and a good measure of the evening with J.T., going over everything we knew, recounting even the smallest of details. After he failed to raise anyone on the radio, he tried the internet, which did not work either, and then flipped through thirty stations on the large TV, getting empty channel after empty channel, before giving up and finally admitting defeat.

At one point, I asked him about the aerobics class that was underway when we arrived. It was an odd thing to be doing, and despite our situation, I could not help but inquire about it.

"I find it helps us to focus," he replied. "Clears the mind of distractions and puts everyone in a relaxed state."

I nodded politely, deciding that dancing in the woods to Madonna was the last thing that would put me in a relaxed state.

The camp still had a fully working kitchen, thanks to the solar panels and the propane gas tanks installed to fuel the stoves, and J.T. asked if we would join the group for dinner. His only stipulation was that we not discuss the events of the outside world, the virus and collapse of society with any of the other people staying at the retreat. He said he would like to break it to them in his own way and time, and since we were his guests, I acquiesced to his wishes, albeit with reservations. Personally, I thought they deserved to know so that they could make up their minds what to do, but it was not my place to interfere, so I kept the feelings to myself.

After a hearty meal of lasagna, prepared by the personal chef that accompanied the group whenever they came up to the retreat, we sat back and relaxed, talking among ourselves. Everything felt so normal that it was hard to believe we had been running for our lives twenty-four hours earlier, but I made sure not to let the spa-like atmosphere and good food distract me from the fact that we were in very real danger.

After dinner, J.T. led us to our accommodations, a cabin with a wide porch and symmetrical six pane windows on each side of the door. Bidding us a good night, he left us and disappeared into his own cabin.

"He seems to be taking things very well," I said, watching him go.

"A bit too well," Clara agreed. "Maybe he still doesn't really believe us."

"He ought to. He spent enough time trying to get an answer on that radio and getting nowhere," Emily said. "Not to mention the fifteen minutes he spent flipping through empty TV channels looking for CNN."

"His loss if he doesn't." I didn't really care if J.T. believed us. Tomorrow we would resume our trek southward toward New Haven. If J.T. or any of his group wanted to tag along, that was fine. This place might feel safe, but I had a feeling that if we lingered, we would regret it. "Come on, let's go inside." I climbed the porch steps, holding the cabin door open for the others to enter, then stepped into the cabin and closed the door behind me.

We explored our new digs. The cabin was spacious. A central

room was set up with a small kitchen and dining table on one side and a lounge area on the other, complete with an overstuffed sofa and two chairs arranged in front of a fireplace. Just as in J.T.'s cabin, there was no TV, but there were a couple of board games and a deck of cards on a side table next to the sofa. Two doors, one set at each end of the cabin, led into a pair of bedrooms, each with two twin sized beds. I opened the fridge, happy to see it stocked with various types of soda, bottled water, and a selection of snack foods. The freezer compartment held pop tarts, individual sized servings of ice cream and mini pepperoni pizzas, among other things.

"This place isn't half bad." Darwin flopped down on an overstuffed sofa against the back wall and put his hands behind his head. "Sure beats the accommodation from last night."

"This is the best place we've stayed in so far," Clara said.

"Hey," Darwin protested.

"Sorry," Clara replied. "The motel was a bit run down though."

"Yeah," Emily said. "And this place doesn't have a crazy waitress running around."

"Or bedbugs." Clara grinned.

"The motel did not have bedbugs." Darwin feigned a hurt look. "I didn't see anyone complaining about it."

"Speaking of beds, we should assign rooms," Clara said. "I vote that we girls take the room on the left, since it's closest to the bathroom."

"No." Emily sat down on the sofa next to Darwin. "That doesn't make sense."

"Huh?" I shot her a look. "Why not?"

"What if something happens in the night?" Emily said. "What if crazies find us or the motel beasts attack again? We'd be much too vulnerable."

"So what do you suggest?" Clara asked her.

"I think I should take a bedroom with Darwin, and you take

the other room with Hayden. That way if we need to defend ourselves, there's a man in each room."

"Makes sense to me." Spending the night with Clara sounded much better than spending it with Darwin. I turned to her. "What do you think?"

"Sure. Sounds great." Clara's eyes lit up. "I mean, if it's what Emily wants."

"Don't I get a say?" Darwin raised his hand as if he were a student asking to go to the bathroom.

"You don't like that idea?" I asked him.

"Oh no, I love it," Darwin said. "I just wanted to say that for the record."

"So, that's it then," I said. "I'll bunk with Clara, and you two can take the other room."

CHAPTER FIFTY-TWO

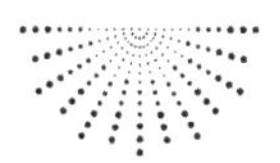

THE BEDS WERE SURPRISINGLY COMFORTABLE. I crawled between the sheets and put my head on the pillow, closing my eyes and relaxing for the first time in days. I looked forward to a full night's sleep. For once we didn't need to keep guard, and it was a wonderful feeling. We made sure the door was locked and the windows were secure, but the cabin felt a lot safer than the motel room.

After making our sleeping arrangements, we'd taken turns to shower. The girls went first, followed by Darwin, and then finally it had been my turn. By then the water was only lukewarm, but it didn't matter. I was happy to wash off the grime from the trek through the woods. It wasn't long after we had showered that we retired for the night. Everyone was exhausted, and I'm sure we all looked forward to a clean, soft bed.

I heard Clara moving around as she prepared for bed. There was a rustle of fabric and I imagined her slipping her jeans off, but I didn't open my eyes. Outside in the lounge area, there was movement, and then the toilet flushed. I wondered if Emily had changed in the bedroom or if she'd made use of the bathroom to undress. I found it hard to believe that she harbored any feelings for Darwin. But then again, she was the one who came up with the idea of cohabiting.

"How's the bed?" Clara asked.

"Heavenly," I replied. I stretched out, relishing the cool feel of the bedclothes on my skin. I'd undressed quickly, discarding my clothes in a pile next to the bedroom door, and now wore only my boxers. I made a mental note to pick up some new undergarments if we ever came upon a store. Three changes of underwear might be good for the short weekend trip to New York that I'd planned, but after days of trudging through woodlands and along deserted highways, they had become less than adequate.

The light clicked off.

I opened my eyes.

Clara was moving across the room. For a moment I caught sight of her smooth, pale skin highlighted against the black fabric of her bra and panties, and then she pulled the covers back and climbed into the other bed, putting her head on the pillow and turning to face the wall.

I lay there for a while, unable to sleep, the events of the past few days churning in my mind, and then I heard Clara softly weeping.

"Are you okay?" I asked.

"I'm fine," Clara said, still facing the wall. She sniffed. "I thought you were sleeping."

"No." I slipped from my bed and padded across the room, then perched myself on the edge of her bed. I reached out and placed a hand on her shoulder. "Everything will be okay."

"I wish I believed that." Clara turned now, facing me. Tears streaked her face, and her eyes looked puffy in the dim light. "I'm sorry. I know I should be stronger than this."

"You've been incredibly strong," I said.

"Not really." She shook her head. "All I can think about are my parents, my brother, my friends. The chance they are still alive is so small. I wish everything was back to normal, that none of this ever happened."

"We all do." I didn't know what else to say.

"I don't want to be alone right now." She looked at me, her eyes wide and wet.

"You aren't. I'll be right there." I nodded toward the other bed.

"No, I don't want to be alone." She lifted the covers, inviting me in. "Please?"

"Of course." I lifted my legs and slid in next to her, wrapping my arms around her, pulling her tight.

"Thank you." She nestled into me, putting her head on my shoulder. I felt her breasts pressing against me, her bare skin warm and soft. "Promise me we'll make it out of this?"

"We will." I ran my fingers through her hair, let my hand stroke her back. "We have to."

"I hope so." She lifted her head, her lips finding mine. She kissed me, the touch lingering and sweet, and then she looked into my eyes for the longest time before putting her head back down and closing her eyes.

I held her close, listening to her breathing grow rhythmic and shallow as she fell asleep, and then, finally, I drifted off too.

CHAPTER FIFTY-THREE

I AWOKE TO THE sound of someone pounding on the cabin door.

I sat bolt upright in bed, blinking the sleep from my eyes.

Clara stirred next to me. "What's going on?"

"I don't know." I jumped from the bed and searched for my pants, finding them in a pile near the bedroom door.

"What time is it?"

I glanced at the alarm clock next to the bed. "Just gone seven o'clock." I pulled on my shirt and pants, and made for the door as a second frantic knock came. "Alright, I'm on my way!" I shouted, pulling the bedroom door open a crack, then closing it again behind me to afford Clara some privacy while she dressed.

I crossed the kitchen toward the front door as Emily and Darwin emerged from the other bedroom.

"Who is it at the door?" Emily asked. "It's very early."

"I know. I was hoping to sleep a little longer." I gripped the door handle and opened it.

J.T. was standing on the other side, his face ashen.

"They're all gone." He spoke the words slowly.

"Who?" Emily asked him from over my shoulder.

"Everyone." J.T. looked shaken. "There's nobody left except us."

"How is that possible?" Darwin exclaimed. "They were all fine last night. We ate dinner with them, for heaven's sake."

"I know that," J.T. said.

"Maybe they got spooked when you told them about the virus, the crazies," Emily said.

"That's just it. I didn't tell them yet. I was trying to figure out the best way to do it." He motioned towards the vehicles parked at the other side of the clearing. "Besides, the bus is still here. How would they go anywhere without the bus?"

I heard the bedroom door open, and Clara emerged. She had brushed her hair and put on a fresh shirt. "It's happening again, just like it did back at the gas station."

"We don't know that," I countered. I hoped there would be a rational explanation for the missing people. If they really had disappeared, it meant that whatever had happened was still happening. I didn't want to wake up alone one day, with Clara missing.

"Did you search all the cabins?" Clara hovered by my side. She reached down and took my hand.

"Yes. All of them. Yours was the last one," J.T. replied. "For a moment I thought you might be gone too."

"We should search again, to be sure," I said.

"What's the point?" J.T. leaned against the porch railing. "This place is so small. There's nowhere else they could be. Everything was fine until you showed up."

"You're not suggesting that we had anything to do with your people vanishing, are you?" Clara was indignant.

"Well, it seems mighty strange that you arrive, four strangers wandering in the woods, with a nutty story about monsters and insane people and the end of the world, and then this happens the very next morning." There was a hint of anger in J.T.'s voice. "You do the math."

"Now look here–" I took a step toward him.

"Don't." Clara held my hand tight. "He's just upset."

"Damned right I'm upset." J.T. paced on the porch. "I think it's warranted under the circumstances, don't you?"

"I still think we should check the camp again," Darwin said. "Maybe someone else survived."

"No one survived. Aren't you listening to me? The place is a ghost town."

"Even so..." I agreed with Darwin. It was worth making sure.

"Go ahead. You won't find anyone." J.T. spat the words, his face contorted with fear and shock.

"We'll see." I pushed past him and walked down the steps, making my way toward the next cabin over, with the others at my heels.

I opened the door and peered inside, but it was empty, just like J.T. said. As was the next one, and the next. By the time we'd searched every cabin, I was disheartened. Just when we'd found a group of people unaffected by the events of the last few days, this happened. It wasn't fair. Finally admitting defeat, I turned to the others. "What now?"

"We move on, I suppose," Clara said. "There doesn't seem to be much point in staying here."

"How could all those people vanish?" Darwin shook his head in disbelief.

"I don't know." I could feel the frustration rising within me like a black tide. "But they did."

"Is it happening again? Are we going to black out?" Emily looked scared.

"I don't think so," I replied. "I feel fine."

"So do I," Clara agreed. "But I don't want to hang around here any longer than necessary, just in case."

"I hear that." I was thinking the same thing. Whatever was

happening obviously didn't happen everywhere at the same time. If this place had survived for days after the event, then maybe other locations did too. Was that what New Haven was, a place that hadn't been affected? I could only hope. Right now though, we needed to pack up and get the hell out of here. I turned to walk back to the cabin where J.T. was still pacing on the porch, but I only managed one step.

"Look." Emily pointed toward the tree line.

As one, we turned and looked.

I spotted a figure emerging from the darkness between the trees. It walked slowly, weaving a little as it went. It wasn't until the figure entered a patch of sunlight that I realized it was a woman of about forty. Her long hair, which at one time might have been beautiful, was now matted to her head. She wore a nightdress, the fabric dirty and ripped in places. Doughy pallid skin showed through the tears.

"What's she doing?" Emily asked.

"I don't like this." Internal alarm bells were going off. "I don't like this one bit."

The woman was in the clearing now. She stopped and looked at us, a dull expression on her face.

I saw J.T. dismount from the porch, a look of relief on his face, and knew instantly what he was about to do.

"J.T. Stop!" I shouted a warning. "Don't."

"It's alright, she works for me. It's Elise Jenkins." But he faltered, hesitating.

"Stay where you are. Don't move any closer." I turned to the others, keeping an eye on Elise. "We should pick up our gear and get out of here. I have a feeling this place is about to become very unwelcoming."

"What about her?" Darwin asked, nodding toward Elise.

"Don't lose sight of her. If she starts toward us, run." I ushered everyone towards the cabin.

We took it slow and steady across the clearing, not wishing

to make any sudden moves that would draw more attention than we already had. Elise watched us, slack jawed and vacant, her arms dangling at her sides. She did not move toward us, and for that I was grateful.

When we reached the cabin, Emily and Clara ducked inside to collect our packs, which we could not afford to lose. The rest of us stayed at the base of the steps, watching Elise.

J.T. looked at me, his eyes wide. "What's wrong with her?"

"She's crazy, that's what," Darwin told him. "And not the life of the party crazy. More like munch on your raw flesh crazy."

I glanced toward the cabin, willing the girls to emerge, then back to Elise. She hadn't moved. Perhaps she was summing us up, or maybe it took a while for things to process now. Either way, she wouldn't stay still for long, and I didn't want to get into a scuffle with her. My encounter with Alice, the crazy server, hadn't been pleasant, and I had no desire to repeat the experience.

Finally, after what felt like an eternity, the cabin door opened and the girls appeared, backpacks in hand.

"About time," I muttered. "Let's go. We'll make for the road." I pointed toward the track leading from the clearing where the bus sat.

"She's moving." Clara looked toward Elise, who now stumbled forward, her movements uncoordinated and erratic.

"She doesn't look very dangerous," J.T. said.

"Trust me, you don't want to find out," I replied. "If she's anything like the other crazies we've encountered, she can move at a pretty good lick if she wants to."

"Are you sure she doesn't just need help?" J.T. was still struggling with the concept of crazies.

"I'm sure." Who knew how many more of J.T.'s staff were wandering around the woods in a stupor. "Trust me."

"Can we go now?" Darwin was eyeing Elise with a look of loathing on his face. "I don't think I like it here anymore."

"Come on." I took my pack and made for the road on the other side of the clearing with the others a step behind me. J.T. lingered for a moment, then hurried to catch up.

We reached the midway point. Now we were well and truly exposed, out in the open. If any more crazies came out of the woods from another direction, we might be trapped. I tried not to think about it and pushed on.

It turned out that it wasn't the crazies we needed to worry about.

"What's that thing?" J.T. stopped in his tracks, looking back toward Elise.

I spun around, a writhing fear clutching at my stomach. Even though I hoped I was wrong, I knew exactly what I would see when I looked.

The beast was a few feet behind Elise, stalking her. It moved, crouched down on all fours, creeping up without making a sound. Elise was unaware of its presence.

"We have to do something." J.T.'s eyes were wide with horror. "It's going to kill her."

"Yes, it is." It was a given. I remembered the frenzied attack back at the motel and our encounter with the beasts before we fled into the woods. "Rather her than us."

"She's still human." J.T.'s face was red. I saw a vein throb on his temple. "We can't just leave her."

"Yes, we can." The force of Clara's words surprised me. She grabbed J.T. by the arm, steering him forward. "If we help her, we all die."

At that moment, the beast made its move. It shot forward, a blur of muscle and teeth landing on the defenseless woman's back. Elise toppled forward, but she didn't try to break her fall. Instead, her face hit the ground with a dull thud. Blood sprayed like a fine rain from her nose and mouth.

The beast rolled her over and slashed with its paw. And then again. Elise was making mewling sounds, not really a cry for help, but more like whimpering.

Another blow glanced off her neck, sharp claws gouging and tearing the flesh, and this time the blood arced up in a graceful curve before hitting and soaking into the ground.

The beast opened its jaws and bit down, securing its victim, shaking the prone woman like a rag doll until she went limp. It raised its head and looked toward us.

"Oh shit," Darwin said, a tremble in his voice. "This is not good."

"Move." I pushed Clara forward, then Emily. Darwin stepped around me, but J.T. stood looking at the bloody corpse of his employee and the beast that was now slinking toward us. "You too." I reached out and grabbed his arm.

"Get off me." He swiveled, his face full of fear and anger.

"If you don't move, you're next." I gripped his arm. "Pull yourself together or you will die here today."

At that moment, two more beasts emerged from the woods. They fixed their eyes upon us. Then, as if making a silent decision, all three shot forward, moving faster than I would have thought possible, closing the gap between us much too fast.

CHAPTER FIFTY-FOUR

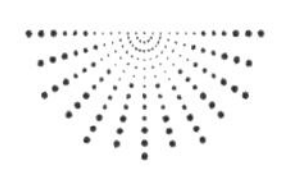

"RUN!" I SCREAMED the command at the top of my voice.

J.T., who until now was acting dazed, regained some of his will. He turned and fled, following the others toward the road. I waited for him to pass me and I followed.

Behind us, I heard the creatures let loose a shriek of rage. I chanced a glance backward and saw, to my horror, that they were almost upon us, their enormous jaws open and ready for the kill. The lead beast still had blood on its teeth from the attack on Elise, and I had no desire to add to that.

"It's no good!" Clara yelled, panic in her voice. "We'll never outrun them."

"Keep moving. Head for the trees; it will be easier to lose them there." I had my doubts about that, but it beat being pursued in the open where we were sitting ducks.

"No." J.T. pointed toward the school bus. "The bus."

"We'll be trapped."

"Trust me. The bus is our only chance."

"It won't work. Remember what we told you yesterday?"

"Dammit, just trust me. I can get it going."

"You'd better know something I don't," I said to him. Then, to the rest of the group, "Do as he says. Head for the bus."

We veered left, abandoning our prior route. When we got to the bus, J.T. pushed past us and reached out, gripping the passenger door release. As soon as it slid open, we piled inside and yanked the door back in place.

The nearest creature hit the door with a loud thud.

"That was too close." Darwin fought to regain his composure. He gulped down air, his face flushed.

I went over to the window and peered out.

The beasts prowled around the bus like sharks circling a hapless swimmer. Every once in a while one of them approached and sniffed, examining the vehicle, then circled once more.

"They're looking for a way in." I hoped the concertina passenger door was sturdier than it looked. The door had already withstood one direct assault, but who knew how many blows it would take before it caved?

"Let them look all they want. We're getting out of here." J.T. slid into the driver's seat. He reached into his pocket and then cursed. "Damn."

"What?"

"The ignition key. I don't have it. It's back on the desk in my cabin."

"Great. Just freaking great." Darwin punched the closest seat. "We're dead. Good job."

"It wouldn't have started anyway," I reminded him. "Cars don't work anymore, remember?"

"I already told you, it does work." J.T. spun in the seat, looking at me. "We went swimming the other day. There's a natural spring a few miles up the road. The bus wouldn't start. The battery was dead. We charged it up and the damn thing still wouldn't turn over. One of my guys is-" He stopped and corrected himself. "Or rather, was a genius with anything mechanical. He took the starter out, a few other bits and pieces, poked under the hood for a few hours, and got it going again. Don't ask me how."

"You don't know what he did?"

"Not exactly."

"So we can't replicate it on another vehicle if we come across one that has a set of keys." I felt like I was the playing the lead role in some bizarre comedy show. Here we were, with possibly the only working vehicle in thousands of miles, and we didn't have any way to start it up. Worse, the only person who might know how to fix another vehicle was missing. If there was a God, he was surely laughing his ass off.

"Let me look." Clara elbowed past me and approached the driver's seat. She motioned to J.T. "Move. I need to get in there."

"Huh?" He looked at her, surprised.

"Let the dog see the bone." Clara almost pulled him from the seat before taking his place.

"What are you going to do?" I asked. The bus shook as one of the beasts barreled into it. I glanced nervously toward the sound of the impact, half-expecting to see the side window shatter.

"I'm going to get us out of here." She adjusted the seat forward to reach the pedals. "I need something flat, like a screwdriver."

"Where are we going to get one of those?" Darwin said.

"Under the rear seat." J.T. took off down the bus. "There's a small toolbox."

"That's lucky," Emily said. "I don't suppose you have a couple of shotguns back there too."

"Unfortunately, just the toolbox. We're not *that* lucky." J.T. was heading back down the aisle with a blue metal toolbox. He put it on a seat, opened it, and took out a flat-ended screwdriver. "Will this do?"

"Perfect." Clara snatched the tool and went to work, pushing the blade into the space between the ignition tumbler and plastic steering column casing. She grunted with the effort and pried back on the screwdriver.

There was another crash, and the passenger door buckled inward. "Better hurry," I said, eyeing it nervously.

"Almost there." She continued to work on the casing.

"Here they come again." Darwin was at the window. He scooted backward as the bus took another hit. A long, zigzagging crack appeared in the window glass closest to the door. "One more hit like that and the window will go."

"I know." Clara pushed down on the screwdriver, standing and putting all her weight into it. For a moment nothing happened, and then the casing broke away with an audible snap. "Got it."

"Better make it quick. It looks like we're about to get hit again, and I'm not sure we can take another one." One creature had backed up, turning, ready to charge. The other two lingered near the bus, as if sensing they were about to gain access.

"Give me one moment." Clara pulled at the wires leading to the ignition, tearing them from the unit. "There are three wires. We need to connect these two like this." She twisted two of the wires together. The dash lit up. "Good. Now we need the starter wire."

"Careful," I cautioned. "We don't need you electrocuting yourself."

"Well, duh." Clara held the third wire between her thumb and forefinger and sparked it against the other two. The engine turned over but didn't start.

"It's working!" Darwin exclaimed. "Do it again."

Clara touched the wires together a second time. The engine coughed, sputtered, then fell silent.

"Damn." I glanced out of the window. The creature lowered its head, making straight for the weakest point on the bus, the dented passenger door. "Hurry!"

"I'm going as fast as I can." Clara touched the wires together a third time. The engine turned over once, twice, and then right at the last moment, just when it looked like we were doomed, it sprang to life.

"Hell, yeah!" Darwin pumped a fist in the air. "That's more like it."

Clara pushed the bus into first and rammed her foot down hard on the accelerator. "Hold tight."

The vehicle lurched forward as the charging beast reached it, but instead of hitting the door, the creature missed and slammed into the back of the bus behind the left tire. There was a dull thud and the bus slid sideways, the wheels refusing to grip for a moment. Then we were screeching from the clearing, our tires kicking up mud and grass into the faces of the pursuing beasts.

CHAPTER FIFTY-FIVE

WE JOLTED AND bumped down the dirt road; the trees whizzing past. Clara was surprisingly adept at driving the bus, steering it with relative ease despite the occasional curse word whenever the wheels dropped into a pothole or lost traction on the loose soil.

"We did it!" Darwin pumped his fist in the air. "Holy crap, we got away. I thought we were toast for sure."

"And we have a sweet ride to boot. No more walking for us." Emily put her arms around him and planted a big, wet kiss on his cheek. I wondered how close they had gotten last night in that bedroom. Probably not as close as Clara and me, but there seemed to be a change in attitude between them. They were closer.

"Hey," Clara spoke up from the front of the bus. "A little appreciation for the mastermind of this great escape would be nice."

"Sorry, you're right." Darwin looked apologetic. "Good job, J.T."

"Jackass." Clara scowled. "Next time I'm leaving you behind as a light lunch for the slathering monsters."

"You can try." Darwin flopped down in a seat close to the back of the bus, with Emily by his side.

J.T. perched on the edge of a seat halfway back, looking shell-shocked. I understood how he was feeling at that moment. Twenty-four hours ago, he was leading aerobics sessions for his team. Now they were all gone, and he was on a school bus fleeing for his life. It was a hard thing to comprehend, as we all knew first hand.

"Where does this road go?" Clara asked, keeping her eyes firmly rooted ahead. She gripped the steering wheel so tight, trying to stop it jerking every time we hit a bump, that her knuckles had turned white.

"Hey, J.T." I walked down the aisle and nudged him. "Where are we?"

"What?" He looked up at me.

"Where does the road go?" eventually we would end up on paved roads, which would enable us to move faster, but would also present additional problems. There would be other vehicles. Most of them, either wrecked or abandoned. If the going got too tough, we may have to ditch the bus and hoof it again, and I didn't like the idea of that. Much better to know where we were and avoid the major arteries altogether.

"It links up with Route 12." He shrugged, a weary gesture of resignation. "After that it depends on where you want to go."

I suddenly realized I did not know which direction New Haven was in. The bus didn't have a GPS, not that it mattered. Given the state of current communications, there was no chance a GPS unit would work, even if we had one. That left one option, an old-fashioned paper map. Only we didn't have one of those either. "We need to find a gas station, pick up a map as soon as possible. Exactly how far are we from 12?"

"Five, maybe six miles." He turned toward the window, sullen, his face reflecting in the glass. On that face, I saw confusion and misery. "I can't believe you left her there to die like that."

"There was nothing we could have done for her." I placed a hand on his shoulder. "We did what had to be done."

"It was murder." He pushed my hand away. "Murder, pure and simple."

CHAPTER FIFTY-SIX

WE REACHED THE paved road in no time. Thankfully, there were very few cars around, at least on this section, and those that we came across were off to the side or only blocked one lane. The one time we found a mini pile up of three cars, we simply slowed down and nudged the closest vehicle forward with the nose of the bus until we punched a hole through. I was not optimistic about our chances with a larger mess of cars or if we ran across a sixteen wheeler.

Now and again, we passed a house, a few of which looked like they might be working farms, with large barns attached, and equipment sitting idle. Not once did we see any signs of life. The landscape was eerie in its emptiness. I toyed with the idea of pulling over and searching the houses for useful items, such as food, water, sleeping bags, and blankets, but there were always more houses, and after our latest encounter with the beasts I didn't want to risk running into more of them or any crazies that might be lurking around.

Now that we were on pavement, I settled into the seat to the right of Clara, across the aisle behind the passenger door. J.T. was still in a world of his own about halfway back. Darwin and

Emily took a seat together at the back, next to the rear door. Under other circumstances, I would have made a joke about that, but now was not the time or the place, and I was in no mood to fool around.

"How much gas do we have?" It occurred to me that we would need to either refuel at some point or abandon our escape vehicle. With no prospect of getting anything else running, that would mean we were back to walking, something I was not keen to do. How we were going to get gas into the bus if the fuel pumps had no electricity was another matter. We could worry about that when we needed to.

"Half a tank." Clara glanced down at the fuel gauge for a moment, then returned her eyes to the road ahead. "I don't know how far that will get us. I can't imagine this thing gets good mileage."

"I'm sure it's horrendous. I'd be surprised if we get six to the gallon, especially on these roads." I remembered an old truck my father used to own. It was a guzzler, getting about nine in the city and eleven highway. This was a much heavier vehicle, and judging from the cloud of diesel fumes I could see spewing behind us, it wasn't exactly running lean. "It should have a pretty big fuel tank though, at least sixty gallons, so that should net us about a hundred and fifty miles if we're really lucky."

"How far away is New Haven?"

"If we were on the Interstate, maybe a hundred and seventy miles, give or take," I said. "But we'll need to take back roads, with the main roads impassable, and that will up our distance considerably."

"So we'll run out of gas before we get anywhere near."

"Unless we can somehow fill up." I leaned forward. "But the big problem is that we don't know where we are right now. We'll need to get a map or we may end up miles out of our way."

"Well, that much I can help you with." Clara eased up on the pedal, slowing the bus. "Look."

Up ahead on the right, we were approaching a building. It was set back from the road, with parking for six or seven cars at the front and another parking area to the side. A few cars occupied the closest spaces to the door, one with its door wide open, but there was no sign of life. As we drew closer, I could read the lettering above the door.

GIBBS GENERAL STORE

Est. 1958

Hand stenciled signs hanging in the windows advertised local cheese, beer, and farm fresh eggs, all of which sounded great, except the cheese and eggs were, no doubt, past their prime since they were festering in a building without power. Beer, even warm, sounded like a good idea.

Clara maneuvered the bus to the side of the road and into the gravel parking area, brought it to a halt, and applied the parking brake. Then she fiddled with the wires until the motor sputtered and died.

I jumped from my seat and descended the two steps to the door, looking for a handle to open it. "How does this thing open?"

"I don't know." Clara scanned the dash, looking for anything that might operate the door. "I don't see anything."

I pushed on the door, but it did not budge. "Maybe those creatures broke it when they rammed into it."

"Maybe." She looked up, noticing a lever above the windshield. "Hold on a second. Maybe this is it." She pulled on the lever. The doors swung open with a quick whoosh of air.

It was time to shop.

CHAPTER FIFTY-SEVEN

"WHY DID WE STOP?" Darwin made his way down the aisle, a puzzled look on his face.

"I want to pick up a map so that we can figure out where we are, and which direction to head in." I nodded toward the store. "Plus, we can stock up on supplies while we're at it. We finally have room for more than granola bars and baked beans."

"I'm not complaining about that." Darwin stretched, grunting as he did so. "But let's be quick. Knowing our luck, the place will be infested with crazies."

"Looks deserted to me," I said, stepping out of the bus with Darwin right behind. "But we'll keep things brief anyhow. I don't want to linger too long in any one place. Every time we stop bad things happen."

"Maybe this time our luck will change. We're due for it." Clara hopped out of the bus, put an arm around me, and dropped a light kiss on my cheek, the gesture intimate and loving.

"I think my luck changed last night." I let my hand wander up her back.

"Cut it out. There will be enough time for that later." She squirmed out of my grasp, grinning. "You know what I meant."

"A guy can try." I saw J.T. stand and walk down the aisle, his figure dark through the bus windows. He appeared in the doorway. That left one person. I turned to Darwin, "Where's Emily?"

"Still on the bus." He scratched his head. "She wasn't feeling well, said she had a headache. I told her to stay where she was and rest up. There's no need for all of us to go in, right?"

"No." I hoped it wasn't anything serious. We'd been pushing ourselves for days now, and it was bound to take its toll. "Maybe we can find some aspirin while we're in there."

"I'll stay here." J.T. looked down at me from the bus doorway. "I can keep an eye out, make sure we aren't surprised."

"Up to you." I shrugged. "But are you sure you don't want to come in and pick up some stuff for the road?"

"Yeah." He met my gaze. "I'm sure."

I sensed an edge of hostility in his voice, but I was too road weary to press the issue. I turned to the others. "Let's go."

We set off across the parking lot toward the store. It was a little dilapidated, the paint peeling in a few places. Hopefully, it would have all that we needed. As we walked, Clara turned to me.

"Can we trust him?"

"Who?"

"J.T." Clara looked worried. "He was awfully keen to stay on the bus."

"He was rather, wasn't he?"

"I hope he's not up to something. He's not exactly enamored of you." Clara had also noticed the hostile edge to his comments.

"He blames me for leaving his friend back in the clearing. He thinks we should have saved her."

"There was no saving her. She was one of them." Clara took my hand, squeezed it, reassuring. "If that beast hadn't gotten to her, we'd have had to take her down. Either way, she was as good as dead the moment the virus hit her."

"I know." We were nearing the store. "Try telling that to him though. As far as he's concerned I let her die, I murdered her."

"You didn't," Clara said. "Of course you didn't."

"He'll come around. This is all new to him, the world as it is now." We reached the store. I mounted the steps and tried the door, pleased to find that it opened easily. "Unlocked."

"See, things are going our way," Clara replied.

"Of course, if we can get in, so can crazies," Darwin added. "So maybe we should be a little less enthusiastic."

"Who said I'm enthusiastic?" The last thing I wanted to do was step inside a darkened building, an enclosed space, when there might be one or more insane killers inside just waiting for a hapless passerby to walk into their spider web. "In and out, okay. No lingering."

"Right," Clara said. "Apart from anything else, I don't want to leave J.T. with control of the bus for too long. We're screwed if he takes off with it and strands us."

"Don't forget that Emily is still on it," Darwin said. "She wouldn't let him do that."

"She might not have a choice." I stepped into the blackness inside the building and held the door wide for the others. I waited a moment for my eyes to adjust, then looked around. The store was small, at least by big city standards. Four rows of goods separated by metal shelves stretched away from us toward the back of the building. A row of freezer cabinets occupied the side wall, their contents thawed and spoiled. On the other wall, next to a service counter, stood an ice cream cooler and several vending machines that dispensed everything from bubble gum and bouncy balls to souvenir pennies. I wondered who would bother buying a souvenir penny of such an out of the way place. An odor of rancid meat and rotting vegetables hung in the humid air.

"That looks like a map rack over there." Clara pointed at a rotating display stand on the counter.

I walked over to it, pleased to see that it did indeed contain maps. I turned it until I found what we needed. "Perfect." I pushed the map into my back pocket and then turned back to the others. "Now, let's stock up. If it looks useful, take it." We had the bus now, so there was no point in packing light, and I'd rather have it with me and not need it than the reverse.

"We should split up. It'll make things faster." Darwin grabbed a cart.

"Good idea." I didn't want to spend any longer than necessary in this place. It gave me the creeps. I walked back over and took a cart of my own.

"I'll take the left aisle, you can take the right," Clara said to Darwin.

"I'll do the middle two." I stepped further into the store, scanning the shelves. Thankfully, the place was brimming with packaged foods. Places like this always carried lots of stuff that had a long shelf life and didn't need refrigeration. It made sense given the low foot traffic the store must have gotten, being so out of the way. All the fresh produce would come from local farms, which made it easier to reduce spoilage. I spotted a pack of Twinkies and my stomach growled, reminding me that we had eaten nothing all day. Breakfast had taken a back seat to escaping with our lives. I grabbed a pack and tore it open, pulling a cake out and ripping off the clear plastic wrapping, then bit into it. The taste of sponge cake and sugary cream filled my mouth. It was all I could do not to wolf the whole thing down in one bite. I finished it and plucked out a second one, which met the same fate, before I grabbed several more boxes and dropped them into my cart. It wasn't healthy food, but who cared? If ever there was an excuse for eating Twinkies with guilt free abandon, the world going to hell just might be it. Several boxes of chocolate chip cookies followed the Twinkies into the wire basket on wheels.

In the next aisle, I heard Clara filling her own cart. I called over to her. "You want a Twinkie?"

"Seriously?" There was a hint of mirth in her voice. "You're over there eating junk food?"

"Not just eating it." I looked down at the cart, at the twelve boxes of cakes I'd dropped in there. "I got some for later too."

"Well, in that case-"

"So, you want one or not?"

"Sure, throw it over."

"Here it comes." I took a cake from the box and flipped it up and over the shelf unit. It rose in the air, then fell out of sight. I heard her catch it and rip the wrapper off.

"Thanks." There was a moment of sloppy munching from the next aisle, and then a contented sigh. "Looks like you got the good aisle. All I have is breakfast cereal, sugar, and cake mixes."

"Sorry," I replied, wheeling my cart further along. "But that's the luck of the draw."

"I've got bread over here." Darwin's voice drifted toward us. "It still looks good; the date on it is next month."

"Take it." I reached the end of the aisle and turned to find Clara next to me. Her cart was full of cornflakes, breakfast bars, and canned goods. I spotted several cans of Spam. I looked at her. "Spam?"

"It's protein, and it won't go bad."

"I'm going to have to get damned hungry to eat that. I hate Spam."

"Well, too bad." She flicked her hair from her face and grinned at me. "You will eat what I give you."

"One night of sleeping together and suddenly you're acting like a nagging wife?"

"Damn right," she said. "I don't see anyone else looking out for you."

"True." I leaned in and kissed her, my lips lingering on hers. "Thanks."

"You're welcome."

"Hey." Darwin rounded the corner, his cart filled to the brim with beer, bottled water, sliced bread, and jars of pickles. "Get a room, will you?"

I released Clara, my eyes meeting hers for a moment as I did so. Despite everything, even more than before, she looked beautiful. My heart beat a little faster. Finally, knowing we should get back to the bus, I turned away. "Do we have everything?"

"I think I've covered all the bases." Darwin held up a roll of toilet paper. "Could have used this a few nights ago in the woods."

"No shit."

"Actually–"

"Funny." I noticed a pile of first aid supplies in the trolley. None of it was prescription, just off-the-shelf stuff like antacid and painkillers, but it was all useful. When we came across a pharmacy, we could raid it for the stronger stuff. "Let's go back. Emily could use some of those pain killers right now." I turned my cart toward the door.

"Right behind you, boss," Darwin said, following along.

As we stepped out into the bright lunchtime sunshine, Clara looked down at her loaded cart. "This has to be the worst case of shoplifting in history."

"Probably," I replied, struggling to push my cart across the gravel toward the bus.

Darwin glanced down at the gun lodged in my belt. "Actually, I think that piece you're packing technically makes what we just did armed robbery."

CHAPTER FIFTY-EIGHT

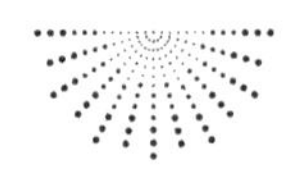

THE BUS WAS STILL SITTING where we left it. Our misgivings regarding J.T. and his motives for staying behind were unfounded. I left my cart near the front passenger door, scooped up an armful of goodies, and mounted the steps. No sooner had I boarded, than I sensed something was different.

The bus was empty. There was no sign of either Emily or J.T.

"There's nobody here!" I called back through the door. "It's empty."

"That's impossible," Clara replied. "I don't know about J.T., but there's no way Emily would leave the bus. Besides, she had a headache."

"Well, she did." I dropped the groceries on the nearest seat. "Do you see them anywhere outside?"

Everything was quiet for a moment, then Clara responded. "No." She climbed into the bus with Darwin right behind, and the three of us stood looking down the empty aisle.

"Where are they?" Darwin sounded nervous.

"Maybe they went to the bathroom?" Clara offered.

"Together? That doesn't seem likely." Darwin shook his head.

"Safety in numbers?" It was all I had. "All I know is they're not in the bus."

"What's that?" Clara pointed toward the back of the bus.

I looked, but could see nothing out of the ordinary. "What?"

"There," she said. "On the floor near the back seat."

This time I saw it. A dark stain between the rows, almost unnoticeable in the gloomy interior unless you were looking right at it.

"That looks like-"

"Don't jump to conclusions." I interrupted Darwin. I took a step forward, keeping my eyes on the dark spot as I made my way down the aisle. Reaching the stain, I stopped, hesitant, not wanting to know what the shiny dark splotch might be, fearing that I already knew.

Clara pushed past me. She knelt next to the strange mark and extended her hand, touched it. Her fingers came away stained a sticky dark red. "Blood."

I looked down the aisle, my eyes alighting on the rear seat where we'd left Emily. An icy dread clutched at me as I saw what lay on it. "There's more on the seat. A lot of it."

"I knew it!" Darwin wailed. "They're dead, aren't they?"

"We don't know that." I hoped it wasn't true, and I didn't want to get his hopes up. But the likelihood was that they were. I could think of no other reason for so much blood to be on the bus, or for our companions to be missing. Had a band of passing crazies killed them, or a pack of beasts attacked the bus and dragged them off while we were inside?

"We have to find them." Clara stood up, her face a picture of resolve. "Even if they are dead, we have to find them."

"About time." Darwin turned to make his way back along the bus, intent upon finding the missing members of the group. He took a step, then stopped. "What the..."

I glanced toward him and froze.

Emily stood in the aisle near the front. Her eyes were wide and bloodshot, her hair unkempt. The front of her shirt and jeans were dark with blood. It was hard to tell if it was her own blood or someone else's.

"Thank God." Darwin took a step toward her.

"No." I exclaimed. I had seen that look before. "Darwin, don't."

He wasn't listening. All he cared about was reaching Emily. He took off down the aisle, opening his arms to embrace her, to make everything better.

She stood, unmoving, until he was almost upon her, and then flew forward, a mindless grunt escaping her lips.

Clara screamed.

Everything slowed down, a slow-motion version of life. I saw Emily leap toward Darwin, saw him stop, surprised, as she reached out to claw his face. He twisted to escape the oncoming fury, but he was too slow by a mile. She hit him hard, her fingers scrabbling at his skin, gouging and raking. Rivulets of fresh blood sprang up on his face, on his arms, as he fell backwards and hit the deck. She stood over him, her teeth bared in mindless, unreasoning rage, eyes darting from side to side. She babbled forth bursts of incoherent sounds. She was wild, and she was about to kill Darwin.

I reached for the gun without thinking, pulled it from my belt, held it aloft in shaking hands. I pointed it at the insane, maniacal thing that had been our friend just minutes earlier.

Darwin flung his arms up as she descended upon him and he pushed her back, though this did not deter her advances for long.

He twisted his head and looked back at us, his eyes widening with terror when he saw the gun in my hand.

Clara stood frozen in fear, her hands over her mouth as if she were trying to stifle the small, whimpering sounds that escaped her lips.

I released the pistol's safety.

"Don't! For God's sake, don't do it," Darwin pleaded even as Emily dropped, heavy, onto his chest, straddling him.

She gripped his hair and slammed his head back into the ground. His skull made a hollow thunk when it impacted the hard rubberized floor. He let out a squeal of pain.

"Do something!" Clara wailed. "Stop her before she kills him."

"How?" I knew the answer. I was holding it.

Emily bent down, biting, her teeth finding Darwin's neck. He howled in pain, his feet thrashing, hands smacking at her back, trying to dislodge her, but she ignored the blows.

I aimed the gun at the exposed top of Emily's head, my hand trembling, and willed myself to squeeze the trigger, but nothing happened. My finger refused to do its work, rebelling against me.

"Do it!" Clara screamed the words. "It's not her, not anymore. Do it."

"I can't." A tear fell down my cheek.

Darwin was moaning now, the sound soft and pathetic. His legs stopped moving, and he lay there, either too damaged to fight back, or giving up the will to survive.

"Then I'll do it." She reached out for the gun, tried to take it from me.

"No." I pushed her hand away. I could not let her take the responsibility, could never do that to her. If anyone was going to do this, it would be me.

"Hey, bitch!" I bellowed the words, a sudden resolve gripping me. I could feel the adrenaline pumping through my veins. "Look at me."

Emily paused, raised her head.

Drops of Darwin's blood dripped down her chin.

I fired the gun.

A flash of bright yellow flame spewed from the muzzle,

followed by a curl of blue smoke. The sound was deafening within the confines of the bus, momentarily robbing me of my hearing. Clara's scream faded, replaced by a high-pitched ringing.

The bullet smacked through Emily's shoulder, sending a spurt of blood backwards. The impact twisted her around, knocked her clean off of Darwin, and sent her sprawling down the aisle. She came to rest, unmoving, near the driver's compartment.

Realizing he was free, Darwin struggled to his knees, his neck a glossy sheen of blood. He looked woozy, dazed. He tried to stand, but fell back to the floor.

Behind him I saw Emily push herself up, swaying for a moment as she regained her feet. She fixed me with those wild, mad eyes, and charged forward, flying past Darwin, heading straight for the cause of her pain.

Without thinking, I pulled the trigger again.

The gun bucked in my hand.

A hole appeared in Emily's forehead, above her left eye, clean and round as if someone had taken a drill to her skull. It looked much too small to be of any consequence.

But it was.

She faltered, staggered. One leg buckled, then the other, and she toppled backwards into the aisle. Her dead eyes stared up toward the roof, the sparkle within them fading. Her hand twitched once, twice, then lay still.

Darwin let out a howl of anguish.

He crawled toward Emily, reached out, held her hand. He raised his head, his eyes finding mine, accusing me. "What have you done?"

He lifted her shoulders, cradled her in his arms, bending low to touch his head to hers. A small cry escaped his lips.

"What have you done? What have you done?" He repeated

the words over and over until they were lost within the sobs that wracked his body.

I stood there, the gun still clutched in my outstretched hand. I was numb, cold. The words fell on my ears, and in them I heard his bitter accusation. I knew very well what I had done, and it sickened me.

CHAPTER FIFTY-NINE

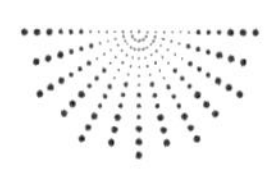

FOR THE SECOND TIME in a week, our world changed.

The immediate threat over, we took care of Darwin, patching up his wounds as best we could with the first aid kit-the same one Emily had used on him a few days before–and laid him across the seat.

His wounds were bad. The cut he'd gotten back at the motel had opened again, the stitches unable to withstand the attack by the same person who had stitched them. The wound didn't look infected, so we did our best to emulate the job Emily had done, but neither of us knew what we were doing. It ended up a little wonky, and nowhere near as tight. It was better than an open wound, though.

As for the rest of his injuries, he was cut up and bruised, with a fair-sized chunk of flesh missing from his neck. How Emily had missed the jugular was a miracle. We also suspected that he was suffering from a concussion, thanks to the number of times his head hit the floor of the bus. He really needed a doctor. The best we could do was to keep him comfortable and hope there were no injuries we couldn't see.

With Darwin, our most pressing concern taken care of, we

turned our attention to other matters. J.T. was still missing, and we needed to do something with Emily, who lay in the aisle, her dead eyes watching our every move.

We took the body between us, Clara at one end, me at the other, and struggled to carry her from the bus. There was a shovel behind the general store, an old thing with a worn wooden handle, but it was good enough. We dug a hole near the side of the store and placed our friend into it, covered her with earth, then found a rock to serve as a headstone. I used a smaller stone to scratch her name and the date on the surface of the rock, then collapsed next to the shallow grave and cried. Clara knelt next to me and held me tight, her hand stroking my head, her tears mixing with mine.

We stayed like that for a long time, neither one of us willing to move, and then, as if reaching an unspoken understanding, we got up and walked back toward the bus.

CHAPTER SIXTY

WE FOUND J.T. about an hour later among the trees on the other side of the road. It was hard to tell exactly what had happened, how he'd come to be lying dead on the forest floor, but I could guess.

His body was covered with bite marks, his neck was nothing more than a raw, open wound. It looked like he'd been half-eaten by wild animals, but I knew it was not animals. The small indentations where teeth punctured the skin, human teeth marks, left no doubt who was responsible. The forest floor was wet with blood. Unlike Darwin, she'd found his jugular. He must have bled out in seconds.

It didn't seem right to bury him next to Emily. She was our friend. J.T. we barely knew. So we buried him where he lay, using the same shovel that dug our friend's grave.

Afterward, our grisly chore complete, we went back to the bus and climbed aboard. Clara went to work cleaning as much of the blood from the floor as she could with a roll of paper towels from the store. I knelt down and helped, removing all traces of the events that had occurred that day.

I found the pistol on a seat near the back. In my daze, I must have dropped it after shooting Emily. Or maybe I put it there later, still in shock. I weighed it in my hands, looked at it, and pondered what to do next. Then I went to the front passenger door and threw the gun as far from the bus as I could. It landed somewhere among the undergrowth and disappeared from view.

With nothing left to do, I slumped down, exhausted, into a seat. Clara took the seat opposite. She looked over at me and spoke for the first time since we had buried Emily.

"Is there any point in going on?"

I glanced at her. "Of course there is."

"How could things have changed so much, so quickly?"

The question hung in the air. I was not sure if it was meant to have a reply, or if it was rhetorical, a statement upon our current situation. In the end I mumbled, "I don't know."

After that, we lapsed back into an uneasy silence until the day transitioned to night. Long shadows pushed their way into the bus, crept along the aisle, fingers of darkness that clutched at the seats and transformed them into barely recognizable shapes in the gloom. I wanted to turn on the overhead lights, cast the darkness away, but that would drain the battery, and we could not risk losing the only transportation we had. The bus was more than just a set of wheels. It was our castle, our shelter from the elements, our defense against whatever might lurk in the darkness outside. So, I kept the lights off and let the night claim the bus.

On and off throughout the evening, I checked on Darwin. He slept most of the time, a fitful sleep punctuated by bouts of incoherent words snatched from whatever bad dreams plagued him.

Eventually, an aching tiredness overtook my body. I took a seat and settled in for the night with a blanket pulled up to my chin. Clara took the seat next to me and wordlessly worked her way under the blanket, her body warm against mine. I closed my eyes and was asleep in a matter of seconds.

CHAPTER SIXTY-ONE

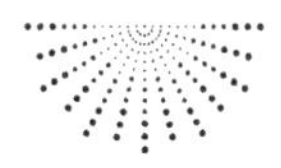

I WAS IN AN open field running.

The horde of crazies was almost upon me, gaining ground every second, but I could do little to pull away. It was like I was wading through air as thick as mud. I risked a glance behind, knowing what I would see, dreading it.

Emily was there. She led the charge; her face contorted with rage and something else. Hunger.

I willed myself onward, icy fear clutching at my heart. Up ahead I saw the tree line, the entrance to a dark forest. If I could make it there, I might stand a chance of losing them.

"Hayden!" Emily called out to me, her voice soft and gentle, belaying the truth of what she intended to do when she caught me. "Join me, Hayden. I forgive you."

Not a chance. She would never forgive me if I could not even forgive myself. I took a deep breath and battled on, the constant fight to move my heavy legs, sapping my energy. Even so, I reached the trees.

"I need you, Hayden," Emily said, and I heard her even though she had not yet reached the forest.

"No!" I shouted the word. "I killed you."

"And you are forgiven."

I could hear them now, crashing through the undergrowth, searching for me.

I had to keep moving.

Suddenly I realized that crazies were not the only ones in the woods. There was something else too. A beast from the motel, its enormous jaws yawning wide to display rows of razor-sharp teeth. It moved parallel to me, keeping pace, watching me, waiting for a chance to pounce. I stumbled forward, eager to keep a distance between myself and the muscular, large beast.

It was then that I noticed that my pursuers, Emily and the other crazies, were almost upon me. I mustered all my strength, channeling everything into a fresh burst of speed, but my legs refused to obey.

I glanced down, horrified to see that I was stuck in some sort of bog. Each time I took a step, my foot came away with the ground clinging to it as if I had stepped into the world's biggest piece of discarded bubblegum. Only this sticky gunk wasn't pink; it was rotten, dirty brown, and it smelled like rotting corpses. I gagged as the odor assaulted my nose. I fought to hold my vomit.

"Be with us, Hayden." Emily taunted me, her voice much closer this time. I was losing the race.

"Go away." I didn't want to listen to her anymore, didn't want to hear that sweet, soft voice calling to me after what I had done to her. How she could even be here was a mystery. Shouldn't she be lying in a shallow grave next to a dilapidated general store off Route 12 in Vermont? I remembered burying her myself.

I remembered killing her.

"It's no use. You can't outrun us," she said, and I knew she spoke the truth, for at that moment I felt a cold, dead hand on my shoulder.

The crazies overtook me, surrounded me, and dragged me to the ground. Hands clawed at my clothes, my face and arms. Now I was sinking into the soft earth of the forest floor, with the crazies all over me, pulling and tugging, scratching and biting. I opened my mouth to scream, but a watery mix of dark sludge filled it instead. I could not breathe. I was drowning.

My vision collapsed to nothing more than a pinhole, and in that bright pinhole surrounded by the unending darkness, I saw Emily looking back at me. Then there was nothing but blackness.

CHAPTER SIXTY-TWO

I OPENED MY EYES, suddenly wide awake.

The bus was still dark. Clara snored lightly, the rise and fall of her chest barely perceptible as she slept next to me. Farther back on the bus, I could hear Darwin mumbling in his sleep.

I thought I saw something move close to the front of the bus, a barely perceptible shape against the windshield and the night sky beyond. Brief and fleeting, the glimpse was enough to cause concern. Was there a crazy outside, a beast, or was it just a phantom that lingered from my dream? I had to find out.

I lifted Clara's head and placed it against the back of the seat, then slid out into the aisle as quietly as I could. I brushed her leg in the confined space as I passed, but she barely stirred.

I padded down the center of the bus, my eyes searching for the cause of the movement. The air inside was frigid. I would not have been surprised if there was a white mist escaping my mouth as I breathed, but it was too dark to know. I wrapped my arms around my body to keep warm and pressed onward, but I could see nothing. All was still and quiet. Whatever had roused me from my slumber was gone now. Maybe it really was a holdover from my nightmare, a bleed-through from the deepest recesses of my subconscious.

Still, I continued down the bus to the passenger door and checked to make sure it was still locked and secure. As I turned back toward the rear of the bus, I felt a familiar vibration in my pocket. I reached down and pulled my phone out. The screen was bright, and there was a new text message.

My finger hovered over the icon. I hesitated for a moment. I was becoming increasingly convinced that it was not Jeff sending the messages. I'd had time to think about things since the last one, and they did not sound like something he would send. The tone, the serious to-the-point nature of the texts did not fit with his personality, even if we were in the middle of the worst crisis the world had ever faced. There was no concern, no questions about my safety, no comforting *things-will-work-out* platitudes. He was always so positive, even in the face of adversity. Were we following the advice of a caring brother, or were we headed toward a trap? I didn't know, but I was forming an opinion.

I punched the icon with my finger.

Two words flashed up on the screen.

KEEP MOVING.

CHAPTER SIXTY-THREE

KEEP MOVING? What kind of advice was that? Did we have any other choice? Of course we were going to keep moving.

I felt bothered. How did Jeff, or whoever was using Jeff's phone, know that we weren't moving? This raised a disturbing question. Were we being watched? As much as I didn't want to think we were, it was the only logical way to explain how the sender of the text knew we had stopped.

I pressed the button on the top of the phone, watched the screen go blank, and then pushed the device deep into my pocket. I made my way back to the rear of the bus and slid past Clara, retaking my seat.

She opened her eyes and looked at me. "What's going on?"

"Everything is fine," I said. It was a white lie, but I didn't want to worry her. "Go back to sleep."

"You left me alone. I was scared." She sat up straight. "Where did you go?"

"I thought I saw something move. I thought something might be lurking around outside the bus." This much was the truth. "I went to check it out."

"Crazies?"

"I don't think so. There was nothing there." I put my arm around her.

"Are you sure?" There was a nervous edge to her voice.

"Yes. We are alone." I stroked her hair, running my fingers through it. "It's still early. Go back to sleep."

"I'm not sure I want to." She pressed against me. "I had a bad dream."

"Me too."

"I dreamed about Emily." Her voice cracked when she said the name. "She was coming for us, trying to kill us."

"Me too."

"You did?"

"Yes." I recalled my nightmare, how Emily had chased me, called out to me.

"I'm afraid," Clara said, her eyes brimming with tears.

"Don't be. She can't hurt us now." I stopped short of mentioning the fact that Emily was nothing more than a corpse with a bullet hole in her forehead. Some things were best left unsaid. "We're safe."

"No, we're not," Clara replied, her voice low. "We haven't been safe since you first walked into the gas station last week. Since *it* happened."

"Don't think about that."

"What went wrong?" Clara asked. "What made her flip out like that?"

"I don't know." I wished I could rationally explain the sudden transformation from a sweet, intelligent girl to a crazy person. "She just did."

"We weren't gone very long," she said. "All we did was pick up some provisions. We were away from the bus for twenty minutes at most."

"The text message we received at the barn on the second night warned us that the virus was spreading." It was thin evidence for what happened to Emily, but it was all I had. "She was complaining about a headache when we left the bus. I bet she was already turning."

"Don't say that."

"What?"

"Turning." Clara shuddered. "You make it sound like she became some kind of zombie."

"Isn't that what Clay called them?" Until now, I'd refrained from thinking of the crazies as zombies, but there was a striking similarity. "Maybe he was on to something."

"And maybe he didn't know what he was talking about," Clara shot back. "What makes him such an expert?"

"I'm just saying..."

"Well, don't. Emily was our friend."

"I know."

"And we killed her." I didn't need to see her face to know that Clara was weeping. "We killed her."

"No. You had nothing to do with killing her." I held her tight, wanting to make things better, unsure how. "I killed her. It was my decision, and my finger that pulled the trigger. Her death is on me."

"Her death is on all of us." Clara sniffed and looked down. "Maybe we could have saved her. They might have a cure, an antidote, in New Haven."

"They don't." Emily–our Emily–was long gone by the time that bullet tore through her brain. Whatever she had become might have worn her face, but the thing inside was not our friend. In the end, she was a ruthless, unreasoning killer. J.T. was lying in his own grave thanks to the monster Emily had become. "Even if they did, that wouldn't have helped us here and now."

"But if there is a cure..."

"There isn't. How could there be?" I truly didn't believe there was an antidote waiting for us at the end of the rainbow. If such a thing existed, someone would be administering it, the

National Guard, the CDC or the Army. They would be pushing back against the crazies and returning them to normal, not hiding out in some town in Connecticut, sending text messages to people. Besides, if there were a cure, whoever sent those messages would surely have said so. What better way to lure us there?

CHAPTER SIXTY-FOUR

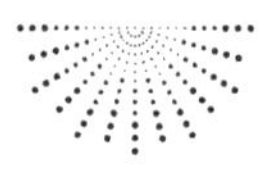

AT FIRST LIGHT, soon after the sun's rays touched the landscape, we set off toward New Haven once more in the big yellow bus with three wires for an ignition key.

We pulled back onto the road after saying our goodbyes to Emily. Each of us stood beside the pile of loose earth that passed for a grave and told her how sorry we were and how much we would miss her. Even though she had only travelled with us for a few days, we had become a team, a sort of surrogate family looking out for each other. I kept my own words brief, feeling the weight of what I had done the previous day. My actions still felt like a betrayal, despite all my logical reasoning telling me I did the right thing. Darwin had regained some of his strength after sleeping for almost fourteen hours. Although he still looked pretty beat up, with fresh yellow and blue bruises appearing about his face and arms, he insisted on being there. When he spoke it was heart wrenching and full of pain, and I turned away, ashamed.

Afterwards, we returned to the bus and drove in silence, each of us absorbing the new reality of our situation, the somber realization that we were light one person. Our family was broken, and there was no way to fix it.

Darwin took a seat as far from Clara and me as possible toward the back of the bus and refused to look in our direction. A part of me was glad about that. I had no words to make him feel any better, and wondered how I would react if the tables were turned. If it was Clara who went crazy, and Darwin who did what had to be done, I had a feeling I would feel much like he did right now.

Once we were underway, I took the same seat as I had the day before, opposite Clara, who once again insisted upon driving. I wondered if taking charge gave her some sort of comfort, provided her with some sense of control over her destiny. Maybe it was just that she liked to drive. Either way, I didn't mind. It allowed me to concentrate on other things, like finding us a viable route to New Haven.

With that in mind, I found the map we'd picked up the previous day from the general store and unfolded it on the seat, flattening it as best I could with the palm of my hand before studying it. The road we were on took us in a southeastward direction for a while, eventually intersecting with Interstate 91. We would need to turn before that and keep to the smaller roads since the highway was sure to be choked. I identified the most likely route and folded the map. Our journey would be a zigzag descent southward, weaving from one back road to another, but there was no choice.

Ordinarily, it would have been a short three-hour drive to New Haven, at least if we were taking the Interstate, but this way would be much longer, perhaps six or seven hours, accounting for wrecked cars and debris in the road.

We drove in silence, none of us feeling much in the mood for idle chatter. The only exceptions were the directions I gave, steering her down one road or another as we followed the map.

This continued hour after hour, and we made good time, although we encountered a few obstacles along the way. At one point we came across a tractor trailer lying on its side, the cargo spilling out onto the blacktop. Luckily, we found enough room to slide the bus along the shoulder, barely clearing the burned and blackened cab. A few miles further on a pair of cars blocked our path, the two vehicles parked facing opposite directions as if they had stopped to have a chat and never resumed their journeys. Clara slowed the bus to a crawl and edged toward the nearest car, bumping it with a jolt and edging the vehicle backwards until it eventually slid away into the other lane. Then she sped up again, and we resumed our trek.

After that it was plain sailing for a while, and I even dozed off momentarily until Clara leaned over and shook me. I had the map, and she wanted to make sure we were still heading in the right direction.

At about one o'clock in the afternoon we passed a gas station, which at first looked like the scores of other gas stations we had passed along the way. One car sat at the pumps, another was partially blocking the road, the passenger side crumpled as though it had been t-boned by something much bigger, although there was no other vehicle to explain the impact. Beads of shattered window glass lay strewn across the pavement. The right wing mirror sat on its own in the middle of the road several yards from the wreck, perfectly upright, as if placed there by some unseen hand.

As we maneuvered past the stricken vehicle, I crossed to the other side of the bus and looked out of the window, noting the damage, and commented. "That's odd."

"What?"

"That Jeep. Where's the car that hit it?"

"Who cares?" Clara slowed and pushed the bus past the narrowest point, barely clearing the stricken vehicle by a matter of inches. "Everything is odd these days."

"I suppose." My eyes picked out a sprawled shape that had,

until we passed the wrecked car, been hidden from view. The body was obviously male by the build and clothes. I recoiled. "That's a body."

Clara followed my gaze. "So what?" She shrugged. "There are bodies everywhere."

"Look at him." I could not help but notice the way the corpse was lying face down, the hair on the back of his head matted with blood. But the thing that really bothered me was the way his hands were tied behind his back, secured at the wrists with cable ties. My blood ran cold. I had a vision of this man kneeling with his hands bound, a gun to his head. "Someone executed him."

"Maybe he was a crazie," Clara said. She looked away, her face pale.

"Then why tie him up first? Why take the trouble to capture him, why not just shoot him?"

"I don't know." She stepped on the gas as soon as we were clear of the Jeep. "And I don't want to find out either."

CHAPTER SIXTY-FIVE

NOT LONG AFTER WE PASSED the gas station, I went back to check on Darwin, who had been sleeping across two of the seats. His head was propped against the window with a jacket behind it. Despite his animosity toward us, I felt it was my duty to make sure he was doing well and to check on his wounds.

He glared up at me, his mouth a thin pressed line, his eyes boring into me. When he spoke, there was little doubt about what he'd been thinking for the past couple of hours.

"J.T. was right." He repositioned himself into a sitting position, wincing. "You are a murderer."

"I'm not getting into this with you," I said. "I only came back here to check your dressings and see if you wanted any painkillers."

"I'm fine." He looked away, out of the window. A deliberate snub. "I don't need any painkillers."

"Your choice." He sure looked like he needed some. The wound he'd sustained back at the motel would be bad enough without the damage Emily had done. "You know where I am if you need me."

"Screw you." His eyes roamed the scenery outside.

I lingered a moment, unsure if I should try and reason with him, but decided against it. He would come around, or he wouldn't. Either way, it was what it was. I couldn't change the past, go back and take back that bullet. Even if I could, I'm not sure I would have. Maybe Emily was better off this way.

I retook my seat and closed my eyes.

The steady thrum of the bus engine lulled me into a half sleep. I dozed, and for once I didn't dream about crazies, or Emily, or monsters chasing me, which was a relief.

"Wake up."

"What?" I opened my eyes, rubbed the sleep from them. "What's going on?"

"There's someone in the road up ahead. They look normal." She was slowing the bus. "What should I do?"

I peered through the windshield. Sure enough, there was a figure standing in the middle of the road, and he looked sane. He waved his arms above his head, signaling for us to stop.

"Well?" Clara glanced at me. "I need to know."

"I'm not sure." The wrecked car was still fresh in my mind, as was the dead man. "Can you see anyone else?"

"No." She shook her head. "Just him, at least on my side. You?"

I leaned over to my side window, scanned the woods on my side of the bus, the road in both directions. "No. He appears to be alone."

"Then I guess we stop."

"What's happening?" Darwin stood up, using the seat as a crutch. Apparently, this new development had convinced him to talk to us. "Did you say there's someone out there?"

"Yes," I replied. "We're going to stop and see what he wants."

Clara spoke again. "Are we certain this is what we want to do?"

"Not by half." Where had he come from? Was he anything to do with the vehicle at the gas station several miles back, and if so, was he a victim that had escaped, or was he the person who had killed the hapless guy lying out on the blacktop? There was only one way to find out. Besides, he was blocking the road, and I didn't fancy running him down. Not today. "I don't think we have a choice."

"We always have a choice," Clara said, but even so, she downshifted and brought the bus to a stop in the center of the road several feet from the stranger.

The man in the road lowered his arms and folded them across his chest, waiting for us.

"Stay here." I stood up, suddenly wishing I hadn't thrown the gun away. What the hell was I thinking?

"No way." Clara rose. "If you think I'm letting you go out there alone-"

"You are." I put a hand on her shoulder and pushed her back down. "I need you in here, ready to drive. We have no idea what this guy wants. He could be harmless, an innocent person caught in a bad situation, like us..."

"Or he could be the guy that killed that man back there." Clara finished my sentence.

"Exactly. I don't want to put us both in danger."

"Well, at least take this." Clara reached down the side of the driver's seat and pulled out the crowbar. "Better to be prepared."

"No shit." I took the metal rod, the weight of it in my hand making me feel a little better about what I was about to do. Not a lot, but a bit. Butterflies swarmed in my stomach.

"Where's the gun?" Darwin walked down the bus, using the seats to support himself in his battered state.

"We don't have it anymore."

"What?" He looked at me. "Why not?"

"I threw it away."

"You did what?" Darwin shook his head in disbelief. "Our only real weapon and you tossed it?"

"I didn't want it anymore. Not after..."

"Screw that." He dropped into the seat behind the driver's compartment. "You're unbelievable, you know that?"

"Alright. I should have kept it." It was too late now. The gun was gone. Even if we went back and looked, we wouldn't find it. "I made a mistake. I wasn't thinking straight."

"Well, that will not help us if this guy is a whack job, will it?" Darwin said.

"Then let's hope he isn't." I reached for the door release.

"Wait." Clara put her hand on mine.

"What?" I paused, my hand lingering next to the release lever.

"Maybe we should think about this."

"I thought we already did." I gripped the door release, activated it. "Just be ready if things go south, okay?"

"Okay." She opened her mouth as if she wanted to say something more, to convince me not to go, but then closed it again.

I wished she would have put up more resistance to the idea of talking to this guy, talk me out of it and drive on, let him jump out of our way as we sped past. Another part of me wanted to save someone, to help them. Heaven knows, I didn't have a good track record of helping people over the past few days. Even J.T. ended up a stiff after being with us for less than twenty-four hours. I hesitated for a moment, took a deep breath, and then stepped down out of the bus.

CHAPTER SIXTY-SIX

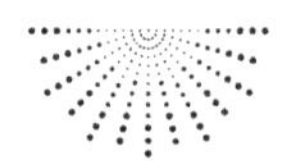

I ROUNDED THE FRONT of the bus and stopped, making sure I was close enough to the door to get back quickly if things got weird. The crowbar felt good in my hands, but not as good as the pistol that I no longer possessed would have. "Afternoon," I said. "What can I do for you?"

"I've been walking for days. Heard your engine, saw you coming down the road," the stranger said. He was tall and lean, in his mid-fifties. He wore a black leather jacket with a white polo shirt underneath. His hair, as black as the coat, was slicked back over his scalp. His face looked like the side of a mountain, rugged and chiseled, the skin pulled over his bones like a mask. "To tell the truth, you're the first people I've come across in a long while, sane ones at least."

"Looks like it's your lucky day then." I was cautious.

"Seems that way, don't it, sonny?" He smiled.

"What's your name?"

"Danny," the stranger replied. "Danny Clements."

"Pleased to meet you, Danny." The stranger looked too clean to have been on the road for days. His clothes were fresh, his hair too neat. I kept a respectful distance.

"Likewise, I'm sure." He flashed a broad smile, all teeth and no mirth. His arms hung at his sides, a relaxed pose, but somehow he didn't appear relaxed. He reminded me of a viper waiting to strike.

"You never said how we can help you." I took a step back toward the bus door. Something wasn't right.

"I didn't, did I, sonny?" He matched me with a step forward of his own. His eyes flashed up toward Clara, still sitting at the steering wheel. "You all seem like friendly folk. Upstanding types. I figured you wouldn't mind lending a guy a hand."

"That depends." My sixth sense was screaming at me to get back in the bus and tell Clara to floor it. I edged another step closer to the door. "How?"

"You have something I want to see." He scratched his head, his nails raking a slow path through the greasy strands of hair. He made the simple gesture look like a threat. "Something I need."

"And what would that be?"

"The bus." He broke out that smile again, just for an instant, and then it was gone. "I want your nice shiny yellow bus."

"I don't think so." I turned toward the bus door.

"Not so fast, sonny boy." He pushed a hand under his jacket, swung it wide and pulled a sawed-off shotgun from a makeshift holster. He leveled the gun at me. "That wasn't a request."

I froze mid-step. For a moment, our eyes locked. I weighed up my chances of getting back onto the bus without being shot. They weren't good.

Danny spoke again, his voice low, menacing. "I'll take the girl too. She's cute as can be. A guy could have some fun with her."

"Like I said, I don't think so." My mind raced. I was only a few feet from the bus. I could make a break for it, lunge forward, and be on the bus before he got a shot off. I looked at Clara. Her hands gripped the steering wheel. Her foot was ready on the pedal. The engine idled. She knew what I was planning. She would floor it the moment I was back on the bus.

Danny had other ideas. He raised the shotgun, leveling it toward the bus, on Clara. "I know what you're thinking, boy. One move and she gets both barrels. She won't look so pretty without a face."

I said nothing. I also made sure not to move, lest he follow through and pull the trigger.

"Now if you don't mind, I'll be taking my wheels." He walked toward the bus.

I watched, helpless as he reached the open door. "Leave her here. Take the bus but leave Clara," I said.

"I'd rather take them both if you don't mind." He waved the gun, motioning toward the door. "Come on then, sonny. Hop on in. I have a feeling your girlfriend will be more amiable with Betsy here pointed at your head."

Really? He named his gun Betsy? In other circumstances, I would have found that amusing. I stepped onto the bus, with Danny right behind. For a moment I contemplated whirling around and snatching the weapon, but I could feel the muzzle at the base of my skull. No doubt his finger was riding the trigger. I'd be dead before I even had a chance.

"Good boy." He motioned for me to take a seat, the gun never straying from me.

I glanced down at the bus. There was no sign of Darwin. Had he escaped out of the back door, leaving us to our fate? It figured. I looked up at Danny. "You won't get away with this."

"Yeah, I think I will." Danny chuckled. He turned to Clara. "Drive."

Clara spoke for the first time since we'd boarded the bus. "Where are we going?"

"That's not your concern." Danny prodded me with the gun. "Now get this thing moving or pretty boy here gets a few new holes in his face."

"Fine." I could hear the anger in Clara's voice. She eased the bus into gear and we moved forward.

"See, that wasn't so hard, was it?" Danny pulled the gun away from my head, but kept it pointed in my general direction. "Now pick it up. We ain't got all day."

We sped up, the woods whipping by faster than before. Danny waited a moment, then, seemingly pleased with our forward progress, reached into his coat and pulled out a walkie-talkie. It was angular, metal, painted dark green, and didn't look like the kind of thing you could buy at Walmart. It looked more like a military model. I wondered where he'd gotten it.

He lifted the unit close to his mouth and pressed the talk button. "Mother Bird to nest, you there? Over."

There was a moment of static, and then there was a new voice. "I read you loud and clear, Gary. Come back."

"Goddammit. Don't use my real name, you moron. It's Mother Bird. Over."

The radio crackled again. "What difference does it make, dude?"

"We went through this already. And say *over* when you finish. Over."

"Sorry." The radio went silent for a second, then hissed again. "Over."

"That's better. I have the bus. We'll be at the crossroads in about five minutes. Tell the others to get ready. Over."

"Will do, Mother Bird. Over."

"Amateurs." Danny–real name Gary–mumbled, and pushed the radio back under his jacket.

"Just can't get the staff, huh?" I looked up. "Why did you call yourself Danny when your real name is Gary? I mean, it's not like we can run to the police or anything."

"Shut it."

"Seems to me you're as much an amateur as the guy you were speaking with." I knew I was needling him, but I didn't care. Chances were that I was going to end up dead anyway, and right now he needed me alive to keep Clara driving.

"We were professional enough to find you and take the bus, weren't we?"

"You were waiting for us?"

"What, did you think I was standing in the middle of the road on the off chance someone would get something working and drive on by?" Gary asked. "Of course we were waiting for you. We saw you when you passed the gas station back there."

"That's impossible." I had a vision of the dead body next to the Jeep, of Gary standing over the poor guy, executing him. "There's no way you could have gotten here ahead of us."

"We didn't. We left someone there to clean the place out. Load up on supplies." He tapped his pocket, the bulge of the two-way radio. "You were just a bonus."

"Lucky us." I glared at him.

"A pretty sweet one though." He glanced at Clara, his eyes glinting with lust. "It's like Christmas come early."

"You touch her and I swear to God, I'll kill you."

"I'd like to see that." Gary poked me with the gun barrel. "Really, I would."

"Put that gun down and I'll oblige you."

"Let me think on it a while." He cocked his head. There was a moment of silence, and then he spoke again. "You know, I'd rather keep the gun if that's all the same to you."

"Asshole." I looked down at the floor, trying to control my anger. As I did, a movement caught my eye.

There, in the seat well opposite, between the first and second rows, crouched as low as he could get, was Darwin.

CHAPTER SIXTY-SEVEN

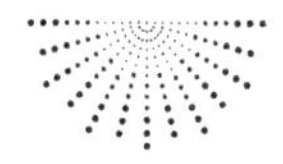

DARWIN PUT HIS finger to his lips. His eyes darted from me to Gary. He lifted his hand, and in it I saw the screwdriver Clara had used to pry the plastic from the steering column back at the clearing.

I glanced frontward. We were approaching a four-way intersection–the crossroads. Waiting for us, standing in the middle of the road, were two men, both armed with semi-automatic rifles. A pistol hung in a holster from each man's belt. Had these guys raided an armory or something?

"Almost there, kids." Gary looked pleased with himself, like a hunter bringing his kill back to the fold, providing food for one more day. He reached out and stroked Clara's face. "I can't wait to show you to them."

She shuddered and pulled away.

I risked a quick peek back toward Darwin. If he was going to do anything, now was the time. If those other men boarded the bus, all bets were off.

He must have read my mind, because from his hiding place there was no way he could have known about the waiting men.

He rose, holding the screwdriver like a knife, and lunged forward.

The blade of the screwdriver hit Gary below his left shoulder and twisted sideways, glancing off his shoulder blade. A few inches to the right and the sharp end of the tool would have pushed through sinew and muscle, piercing Gary's lung, but Darwin's aim was off.

"What the..." Gary staggered forward. He emitted a howl of pain and twisted around, bringing the shotgun to bear on Darwin. "Who the hell are you?"

Darwin dropped the screwdriver, a look of panic etched on his face.

"You know what? I don't give a rat's ass who you are." Gary's finger flexed on the trigger.

Clara slammed on the brakes.

Gary lost his balance. The gun jerked upward as he toppled backward. His finger clenched on the trigger. There was a bright flash, a roar of sound. A ragged hole appeared in the roof of the bus. Daylight pierced the opening, illuminating Gary's face as he fell.

He hit the windshield with a sharp crack and crumpled sideways. The shotgun fell to the floor. It bounced once, twice, then came to rest at Darwin's feet. He looked down at it the way a child might peruse an unexpected gift from a stranger, unsure if they should accept it. Then, coming to his senses, he snatched the weapon up.

Gary lay unmoving in the aisle next to the driver's seat, knocked cold by his encounter with the windshield.

"Give me a hand here." Clara jumped from the driver's seat and knelt next to the prone man, rifling through his pockets.

I pushed past Darwin, glancing outside as I did so. The two men waiting at the crossroads were moving now, running toward us. We only had a few moments before they reached the bus. I reached out to the door release and pulled it. The bus door opened with a whoosh of compressed air.

"Here. Take these." Clara offered me a handful of shotgun shells. She reached under his coat and jerked the two-way radio from an inside pocket. "No point in leaving this with him."

"That's good enough." I looked up. The men were almost upon us.

"Hang on. He might have other stuff we can use."

"We don't have time," I said. Another moment, and it would be too late. "We need to ditch him right now."

I took hold of Gary's jacket and pulled him from the floor, wrestling him toward the bus door. Clara took his legs and together we hefted him to the steps and pushed him over.

I expected him to slide down, but he didn't. Instead, he stuck there with his legs in the air, his head resting on the bottom step.

"They're coming," Clara said, risking a sideways glance through the windshield. She bit her bottom lip, pulling at it with her teeth.

"I know. Get back behind the wheel. Go." I maneuvered myself past Gary. I motioned to Darwin. "Give me a hand."

Clara slipped back into the driver's seat. "Hurry."

Darwin stepped forward, putting the gun on the seat.

"Grab his legs." I reached down, put my hands under Gary's head, and gripped his coat at the shoulders. "Quickly."

Darwin took hold of Gary's ankles, grunting as he straightened, lifting them off the steps.

I took a deep breath, mustering all my strength, and heaved forward.

Gary finally budged. He slid off the last step and toppled off the bus. I rushed back up the steps, waving Clara forward. "Get us out of here."

She threw the bus into gear and stomped her foot on the

accelerator. The bus shuddered, the engine raced. We lurched forward, our wheels spinning for a split second before they gained traction. Then we were off, slicing between Gary's accomplices as they leaped out of the way to avoid becoming road kill, their angry shouts quickly fading as we left them behind.

I turned to Darwin and raised my hand for a high five. He slapped my palm and grinned at me. Our differences put aside, at least for the moment.

CHAPTER SIXTY-EIGHT

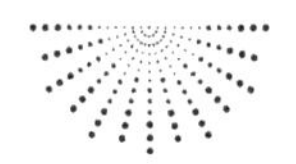

"OH YEAH!" DARWIN whooped. "We did it!"

"And we've got ourselves a new gun." I picked up the shotgun. It felt different from the pistol. Darker. Meaner.

"That was too close," Clara said. "Assholes."

"Let's not stop for any more hitchhikers, okay?" I sat down, my legs suddenly feeling wobbly.

"Works for me," Clara replied. She twisted in the seat and spoke to Darwin. "Good job with the screwdriver. You saved us."

"Not that good a job. I wanted to kill the bastard, not scratch him." He smiled.

"Doesn't matter," I told him. "Without you, we'd be dead now."

"Not all of us," Clara reminded us. "He had other plans for me."

"Don't think about that." I placed my hand on her shoulder.

"Easy for you to say," she replied. "He just wanted to shoot you."

"Well, he didn't have time to do anything," I said.

"We should have killed him before we tossed him out of the

bus." Her voice was hard, emotionless. "People like that shouldn't get to survive."

"Too late now." Her newfound ruthlessness concerned me. Then again, we might all need some of that attitude in order to stay alive in this new world. Things had changed. The rules of society no longer applied. There was no safety net.

"Doesn't seem fair." Darwin reached down and picked up the screwdriver. "It's bad enough dealing with crazies and monsters, now we have to be on the lookout for garden variety psychos too?"

"Just because it's the end of the world doesn't mean all the bad people are suddenly going to play nice," I said, gripping the back of the seat to keep my balance as the bus lurched along at a reckless pace. I was about to suggest that Clara ease up on the gas, figuring that Gary and his goons were far behind us, but I never got that far. It was at that very moment that the back window of the bus exploded inward with a mighty bang.

CHAPTER SIXTY-NINE

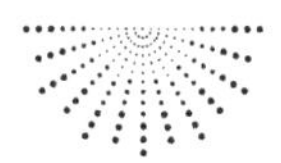

BEADS OF SAFETY glass showered down like glinting crystal rain onto the back seats of the bus. Everything was suddenly much louder.

"What the hell was that?" Darwin leapt to his feet, a look of panic on his face.

"Someone is shooting at us." Seconds later, a bullet whizzed past me and embedded itself into the back of a nearby seat with a popping thud.

"It's Gary and his cronies." Clara glanced up to the rear-view mirror. "They have a truck. How is that possible?"

"Well, we have a bus, don't we?" I raced down the aisle to the back window, grabbing the shotgun as I went. Sure enough, there was a pickup truck right on our tail. It was one of those big quad cab affairs, sitting on raised suspension so high you could almost see under it. A sturdy-looking cowcatcher bumper was bolted to the front. I saw Gary hanging out of the passenger window, a rifle aimed at us. "They must have figured out how to get it working."

"Or they stole it from someone who did," Darwin said, hunkering down between the back seat and the seat in front. "If they knew how to get cars working again, why bother coming after us?"

"Good point." I ducked as another bullet slammed into the back of the bus. A picture of the dead guy at the gas station crossed my mind. Were they driving his truck? "I was hoping we'd sent a message by throwing Gary out of the bus."

"I don't think they got it," Darwin said. "I think we just made them madder."

"Told you we should have killed him!" Clara shouted.

"Too late now," I said. Another bullet flew past my ear and ricocheted off a handrail. "Damn. That was close."

"We'll never lose them in this thing," Darwin said, watching the truck accelerate toward us. "And I don't think they are going to give up."

"Then let's give them something to think about." I knelt on the back seat and pointed the gun through the shattered back window, aimed as best I could, and fired. At the last moment, the truck veered to the left to avoid the gunfire, then swung back in behind us, unharmed.

Gary returned fire, his own aim as bad as mine. As far as I could tell, he missed the bus entirely.

"Again," Darwin said. "Shoot back."

"Hang on. I've got to figure out how to use this thing." I examined the gun, finding the action and pumping it before taking aim again. This time I anticipated their swerve. The truck's windshield imploded.

"You hit them," Darwin whooped. "Oh yeah. Score one for the little guy."

"They're still coming though." I might have reduced their windshield to shrapnel, but I'd missed the driver, my primary target. Worse, it appeared the gun was out of ammo. "I need to reload."

"Hurry," Darwin urged, as another bullet smacked into the back of the bus. "They're aiming for the tires."

"Give me a minute." I'd never loaded a shotgun before. "I need to figure this thing out."

"Rest the gun on the seat," Darwin said. "There's a loading flap in front of the trigger guard. Push the shell in until it clicks."

"How do you even know that?" I dropped out of sight behind the back seat and found the loading flap, then pushed a shell up and in with my thumb. "You don't strike me as the gun toting type."

"I'm not," he replied. "But try telling that to foster dad number three who thought the best way to bond was over a loaded gun. He took me hunting every Saturday for six months. It was pure hell."

"I see." I fired off another shot, surprised to find the truck closer than before, and then called down the bus to Clara. "Can this thing go any faster?"

"Not really." She shook her head. "It's like driving a tank."

"They're pulling beside us," Darwin warned, a grim look on his face. "What are they up to?"

As if to answer him, the truck drifted sideways, hitting the rear of the bus, pushing us toward the road's edge.

"Damn." Clara fought to keep control. "Did they just ram us?"

"Yeah." I shifted position, scrambling over to the side where the truck had hit us. If I could get off one clean shot, I should be able to take out the driver at this range. That was, if the bus didn't veer too much. "Keep us steady."

"I'm trying!" Clara shouted back. "It's not easy."

"I know." I raised the butt of the gun and brought it down against the side window, intending to smash it out and fire at the truck. Instead, the gun skipped on the smooth surface and was almost wrenched from my hand. For a moment, I saw the driver look up at me. Our eyes met. He waved and floored it.

The truck sped past us; the engine screaming as it approached the front of the bus.

"What are they doing now?" Darwin raced down the aisle.

The truck drew level with the front passenger door. A portion of the quad cab's rear window slid sideways. The muzzle of a gun poked out. My heart skipped a beat. They were going to shoot Clara, and there was nothing I could do about it.

There was a flash. My eyes darted toward the driver's compartment, expecting to see her slumped over the wheel, but she looked fine.

For a moment I thought he'd missed. Then I felt the back of the bus drift to the right, saw sparks flying from where I imagined the front right wheel arch to be, and knew that he hadn't.

"The tire!" Darwin shouted. "They shot out the front tire."

The bus pivoted, the front slowing as the back kept going. I felt my stomach do somersaults as the cumbersome vehicle lost its fight to stay in a straight line. We drifted sideways. The truck surged forward to get clear of us.

"We're skidding." Clara sounded scared.

"I know." I ran down the aisle, fighting to keep my balance. "Open the door."

"What?" Clara shouted. "Why?"

"Just do it." I brought the shotgun up. "Now."

Clara reached up and pulled the door release.

As the rear of the bus turned, carried by its own momentum, I aimed the shotgun, waiting until the speeding truck appeared in the doorway, in my line of sight. I fired one last round, all I had time for, through the open door.

I got lucky.

The truck's rear window disintegrated. The vehicle veered left off the road, up over the shoulder, straight into a tree. It tilted almost vertically before slamming back down hard, a curl of dense smoke rising from the hood.

"Got them!" I allowed myself a moment of exhilaration. It didn't last long.

"I can't hold on," Clara said. "Better grab onto something. We're going over!"

I reached out, gripping the back of a seat as the left side of the bus lifted.

Darwin shouted something unintelligible, a curse word perhaps.

Then the bus flipped, tumbling two, three, four times. The windows blew inward, first the right side, then the left. Glass flew in all directions. Everything that wasn't either strapped or bolted down took flight, filling the space inside the bus with a barrage of deadly objects. Baked bean cans became lethal weapons, blunt objects capable of cracking a skull.

Chaos reigned. I had the crazy thought that our bus resembled a snow dome shaken by some almighty hand, only instead of fluffy white flakes it was our provisions and possessions that flew around in the maelstrom.

My feet lifted from the floor. I did my best to hold on to the seat, but it was no use. I hung in mid-air for a moment, my stomach in my mouth, before slamming into the roof. Pain shot through my body. Bright flashes of light danced before my eyes.

The last thing I heard before blacking out was Clara screaming.

CHAPTER SEVENTY

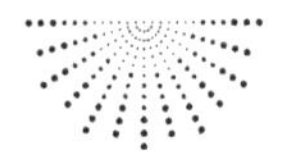

I GASPED AND SAT UP.

"Oh, thank God." Clara crouched next to me. "You're back."

"What happened?" For a moment, my mind was blank. My head hurt. I looked around, surprised to find myself propped up against a tree. "Where am I?"

"The bus rolled." Clara reached out and took my hand. "You took a real beating, hit the roof. We thought you were dead."

"No such luck." Things were coming back now. I remembered the chase, shooting at the truck after it took out our tire. I looked at Clara. "Are you hurt?"

"I'm fine, except for a few cuts and bruises. I was wearing a seat belt. Those school busses are built like tanks." She smiled. "Not that I'd want to do it again, mind you."

"Yeah." I glanced sideways, toward the road. The bus lay on its side. It looked like someone had taken a huge hammer and pounded it. All the window glass was gone, and the yellow paint was now missing in places, replaced by scrapes of bare metal where the vehicle had bounced and slid. Along the road, behind the bus, was a trail of debris. "Boy, we really wrecked that thing." I forced a smile. It hurt my face, so I stopped.

"We'll need new wheels," Clara said.

"I never liked that bus anyway."

I recognized Darwin's voice and turned to find him sitting a few feet away on a fallen tree trunk.

He looked like he'd gone ten rounds with Mike Tyson. His eyes were swollen, and there was a gash on his cheek. His jeans were torn at the knees. When he spoke, I saw he had a split lip. "Damn thing made me feel like I was back at school. Next time let's find a sweet sports car, a Ferrari or something."

"I think we can find something roomier than that." I was relieved that he was still alive.

"What's the point of being the last people alive if we can't have some fun with it," Darwin replied.

"Fun can wait." I reached into my pocket and pulled out the phone, hoping there would be a new message from Jeff. But the screen was shattered, a spider's web of cracks creeping over the surface. The phone was broken, useless. I threw it to the ground. "I guess my phone fared worse than I did."

"Who cares," Clara said. "We're all safe. That's what matters."

"Not too safe." I remembered Gary and the other morons in the truck. "What about–"

"Darwin took care of it," Clara replied.

"He did?" I looked at him, surprised.

"Yeah." Darwin held the sawn-off shotgun aloft. "Me and Betsy went and had a little chat with our friends in the truck."

"You killed them?"

"I did what was necessary." Darwin placed the gun back on the ground at his feet. "They were pretty banged up after their truck hit that tree trunk. You scored a direct hit on the driver, put a hole the size of a grapefruit in his head. The other two were sitting there, trapped in the wreckage. Man, they were in a bad way. It was more of a mercy killing, really."

"You shot them while they were defenseless?" This didn't sound like the Darwin I knew.

"Yeah." He fixed me with a stony stare. "Just like you shot Emily."

"That was different."

"No, it wasn't." He bowed his head, looked down toward the gun. "Seems this trip of ours has made us all into killers."

"We'll talk about this later." I tried to stand, but I still felt shaky.

"You need to rest." Clara moved close to me, put her arm around me. "We can stay here awhile."

"That's not a good idea." I looked toward the wreckage of the truck pushed up against a tree several feet away, imagining the grisly sight inside. "Who knows if there are more of those guys around?"

"If there are they didn't come to the rescue of their buddies," Darwin said.

"I'd rather not wait to see if anyone else shows up." I took a deep breath and hauled myself to my feet. This time it wasn't so bad. I motioned to Darwin. "Come on."

"Where?" He got to his feet.

"There." I glanced toward the wrecked bus. "Let's salvage what we can and get the hell out of here. We were driving for hours before the crash. We can't be that far from New Haven now."

"We don't know how to get there."

"That's why we need to find the map."

"And then what?" Darwin asked.

"And then we walk." I steered him toward the bus, my bruised and battered body complaining. I ignored it. "You're not afraid of a little walking, are you?"

CHAPTER SEVENTY-ONE

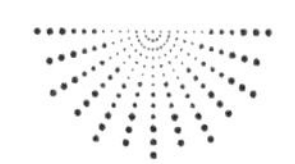

WE LEFT THE BUS behind and walked.

It turned out we were not far from New Haven, and even though there were only a few hours of daylight left, I thought it prudent to put as much distance between ourselves and the scene of the crash as possible.

We rescued most of the supplies, and these we stuffed into our backpacks until they were overflowing. What we could not carry, we left in a pile next to the vehicle. The surplus items couldn't help us, but maybe some other refugee would come past and be glad for the canned goods and packaged foods.

Before we departed, Clara plucked a black marker from her bag and scrawled a message on the back of the bus, warning those who might follow to be careful of strangers.

"I don't want anyone else running into more of those creeps," she said, nodding toward the wrecked pickup.

She was about to add to her message, telling other travelers to head toward New Haven, when I stopped her.

"That's not a good idea," I said.

"Why?"

"Because we don't know who might be see it. The last thing we want to do is tell them where to find us."

"Fine." I could tell she was not happy about it, but she knew I was right.

We walked in silence for a while, each of us lost in our own thoughts. As it had so many times over the last twenty-four hours, my mind wandered back to the previous day and Emily. Things felt different now, and it was unfair that she should die when we were so close to reaching our objective. Worse, the thought occurred to me that we could have saved her, that someone in New Haven might have been able to do something if only we could have gotten her there. As always though, I concluded that she was beyond help, and the chances of a cure for the virus waiting for us at the end of the yellow brick road were slim to none.

And so we trudged on, ignoring the aches and pains that wracked our bodies and the mental pains that had been inflicted upon us over the last few days. Finally, we came over the brow of a hill and saw the skyline of a city dotting the horizon.

"Is that New Haven?" Clara stopped and wiped her brow, a look of hope upon her face.

"I can't imagine what else it could be," I replied, studying the tall buildings that rose out of a forest of greenery.

"Finally." Darwin looked relieved.

"So where do we go?" Clara asked the question we'd all been thinking. "When we get there, how do we find the person who sent the text messages?"

"I have no idea." I'd never been to New Haven before, but from our vantage point, it looked large. "There must be people down there though, if this is a rallying point. We should run into someone pretty soon."

"Well, what are we waiting for then?" Darwin took a step forward. "The sooner we get down there, the better."

"We might even find out what the hell happened." Clara

adjusted the pack on her shoulders. “I for one would like to know why my friends are all dead, and my family.”

“We don’t know that your family is dead,” I reminded her.

“Either way, I want to know who did this and why.” Clara took off down the road in the direction of the city. “And the answer may be down there.”

CHAPTER SEVENTY-TWO

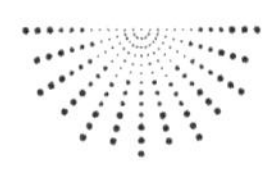

THE SUN WAS SINKING below the horizon by the time we reached the city. At first the rolling hills gave way to a steadily increasing number of industrial buildings and an outlet mall, its parking lot dotted with vehicles. Out of curiosity I took a detour and found a car with the keys in the ignition, the body of an older woman in a floral dress slumped over the wheel. It was a long shot, but if we could procure another vehicle, it would make the last few miles much easier going. I reached in and took ahold of her dress, quelling the sudden onslaught of revulsion that threatened to make the contents of my stomach reappear, and tugged. There was a sharp tearing sound, and I stumbled backwards, a piece of floral cloth clutched in my hand. The woman remained, stubbornly, in the car.

"Give me a hand." I motioned to Darwin.

"What?" His eyes wavered from me to the corpse. "No way."

"Oh, for heaven's sake." Clara pushed past him.

"Go to the passenger side," I told her. "Reach in and push. I'll pull from here."

"Done." Clara ran to the other side of the car and pulled the door open. A moment later, she was in the passenger seat. "Ready when you are."

"On three." I met her gaze for a moment and then focused my attention back to the job at hand. "One, two, three."

As one, we maneuvered the body out of the seat, Clara pushing while I pulled. At first, nothing happened. The woman was unwilling to give up her ride, even in death, but then she slid sideways.

I jumped back as gravity took over and the corpse tumbled out of the car, landing with a sickening dull thud on the concrete, her feet still propped over the door sill.

I bent down and gripped her by the shoulders, dragging her back as I did my best not to think about what I was doing.

Once she was free of the vehicle I climbed inside, pushing the seat back to accommodate my legs, which were longer than our benefactor's. I paused for a moment before reaching out and turning the key, offering a silent prayer that the car would spring to life and grant us a reprieve from further walking. However, no-one was listening. The car emitted a wheezing, coughing sound, but refused to start.

I tried again, but to no avail. Our endeavors had been for naught.

Disappointed, I climbed out.

"At least we tried." Clara rounded the car and put a hand on my arm.

"If only we knew how they got the bus running." I wished, not for the first time, that I'd paid more attention as a teen when my father tried to explain the intricacies of the internal combustion engine.

"If only I hadn't crashed the bus," Clara said.

"That really wasn't your fault." If anyone was to blame for our current predicament, it was me. "I should have told you to drive on when Gary flagged us down. If we'd never stopped, we would still have a set of wheels right now."

"They would have chased us anyway."

"Maybe." I glanced skyward at the steadily darkening sky. "We should find somewhere to settle down for the night."

"I agree." Clara nodded. "Who knows how many crazies are loose out there?"

"Not to mention those things that attacked us at the motel." Darwin spoke up, edging closer.

"So where did you have in mind?" Clara asked. "If we keep walking, we should come across a house pretty soon."

"I have a better idea." I glanced from Darwin to Clara. "I assume you brought the crowbar?"

"It's in my pack. Why?"

"Because I'm going to need you to work your door opening magic one more time."

Clara raised an eyebrow. "What trouble are you going to get us into now?"

"You'll see." I turned and walked across the parking lot. "Come on, we don't want to be out here after dark."

CHAPTER SEVENTY-THREE

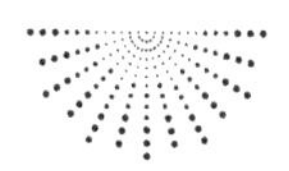

"THIS IS WHERE WE'RE STAYING?" Darwin looked confused. "Wouldn't it be better to keep moving and find somewhere a little more comfortable?"

"Actually, this makes perfect sense." Clara grinned and stepped toward the double doors, the crowbar gripped in her hands. "We can sleep here overnight and strike out toward New Haven first thing tomorrow. Good thinking."

"Thanks," I said.

Clara inserted the crowbar into the space between the two glass doors and pried, grunting, until they gave way with a pop. She pushed inward; the doors opened to allow us entry to *Woodland's Outdoor Superstore*. She stepped across the threshold into the store and stopped. "Well?"

"I don't get it," Darwin said. "How are we going to stay here?"

"They have everything we need," I replied, joining her. I'd seen the camping and hunting superstore as soon as we drew close to the mall. It was hard to miss, with canoes and ATVs lining the sidewalk and a huge red and yellow sign towering over the mall anchor building. "We should barricade these doors before we go any further."

"Good idea." Clara looked around, her eyes alighting on a large display stand full of fishing poles. "What about that?"

"Works for me." The stand looked sturdy, heavy. Even better, it was only a few feet from the doors. I motioned to Darwin. "Give me a hand, will you?"

"This is a dumb place to stay," he said. Nevertheless, he joined me and together we pushed the display over, sliding it up against the doors to prevent anyone from following us in. "What if there are already crazies inside the mall?"

"They won't be able to get in here. The store was closed when things went to hell, so the door leading to the main mall area should be locked." I took off through the store, weaving my way toward the camping section. "Besides, there could be crazies anywhere, so nowhere is really safe."

"Maybe we should have kept going," Darwin said. "We're so close. If this is a safe zone, there should be lots of other people there."

"We don't know where to find them," I replied. "The last thing I want to be doing is wandering the city in the dark. That seems like a good way to get ourselves killed."

"I agree," Clara chimed in. "One more night won't make any difference. Besides, we need rest. It's been a tough few days."

"Amen to that." We had reached the camping gear. I found a display containing fleece sleeping bags and tossed one to Darwin and another to Clara.

"So where are we sleeping?" Darwin caught the sleeping bag with a one-handed grab.

"How about right there?" I pointed toward a break in the displays to a raised dais upon which was erected a green four person tent flanked by two fake trees. "See? They knew we were coming and got our room ready for us."

"Not much of a room." Darwin eyed it with quiet discontent.

"It'll do." Clara stepped forward and pulled down the zipper. "This is certainly safer than being outside."

"I still think we should find somewhere else." Darwin pouted. "There must be a house around here somewhere. We could sleep in actual beds instead of on the floor."

"You want to find somewhere else to sleep, then go right ahead." I shot him a look. My patience was frayed, and any goodwill I was willing to give him over recent events was melting away. "We are staying right here."

"Darwin, get in the tent," Clara said. She looked at us. "We shouldn't be arguing among ourselves."

"Fine." He shrugged his pack off and dropped it to the ground, and then pulled the flap back and climbed in.

Clara went to follow, but hesitated when she saw me lingering. "Are you coming in?"

"Sure. In a few minutes." Everything appeared normal, but I wanted to make sure. "I'm going to take a quick walk through the store and make sure everything is secure and we are alone."

"Are you sure?" Clara bit her bottom lip. "Maybe we should come with you."

"No." I shook my head. "You stay here. I'll be fine."

"Don't be too long."

"I won't. I promise." I reached backward to my pack. My hand closed over the butt of the sawed-off shotgun we'd liberated from Gary. I pulled it out. "Besides, I have this."

"Well, alright." She still looked unsure.

I nodded and turned away. I had only gone a few steps when Clara spoke again.

"Hayden."

"Yes?"

"I'm not sure I could go on without you."

"I know." My eyes met hers, and for a moment I contemplated staying. But another part, a bigger part, knew how vulnerable we were, so instead I kept going, gun at the ready.

I moved through the store, walking among the displays and shelves, careful not to trip. It was dark now, and even though I was worried about drawing attention to myself should there be any crazies here, I found a camping lantern and cranked the handle until the LEDs lit up. It would have been easier to pull a flashlight off the shelf and load it with batteries, but I knew from experience that batteries would not work. Just like our phones and my car battery, they would have drained when things went wrong. The lantern was dynamo powered, and that meant that it worked.

Now that I could see where I was going, I moved a little faster. The store was large, but after a while I found myself on the far side, face to face with a set of glass doors that led into the mall.

I put my face to the glass and peered into the darkness beyond, but everything appeared normal. I could see the vague shapes of seats, vendor carts, and large round floor standing plant pots filled with ferns. I reached out and gripped the door handles, pulling. They rattled, but did not move.

I was about to turn and make my way back to Clara and the tent when something moved out beyond the doors.

I froze, my eyes searching the gloom.

And then I saw it.

Slinking along, keeping close to the wall, was one of the beasts we had encountered at the motel. I clicked the lantern off and took a step backward, afraid it would see me.

It moved at a slow pace, its bulbous head weaving from side to side as it went. At one point it glanced toward the doors, and my heart skipped a beat, but then it moved off without pause, and was soon swallowed up by the darkness.

I stood there for a while, not daring to move, waiting to see if it would return. Eventually, I backed up and walked to the tent, not daring to use the lantern now.

Clara heard me and poked her head out. "Everything okay?"

"Yes." I kept quiet about the beast. It couldn't get into the store, and we had nowhere else to go, anyway. “Everything is fine.”

CHAPTER SEVENTY-FOUR

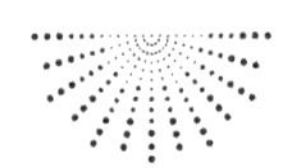

WE LEFT AT DAWN, hiking back across the parking lot and rejoining the road, each of us munching on spicy beef jerky liberated from a stand near the front of the store, next to the cash registers. It was not a perfect breakfast, but it made a change from cold beans and sandwich bread, which had become staple of our diet.

Jerky was not the only thing we took. We also upgraded our small backpacks and now toted fancy lightweight hiking packs with carbon fiber frames. The store was well stocked with guns and ammunition, and it wasn't long before we had brand new rifles in our hands. Before stepping out into the parking lot, I made sure that each gun was loaded and pushed a box of bullets into each pack. My reservations about Darwin carrying a firearm remained, but I reminded myself that he had dispatched Gary's friends with cold precision; it didn't feel right to leave him unarmed. I hoped that he'd forgiven me for what happened to Emily, or that at least he would show some restraint and that I would not find a bullet in my back at some point.

We hadn't been walking for long when the landscape changed from industrial and commercial buildings to urban sprawl. Warehouses and welding shops gave way to subdivisions with names like *Shady Oaks* and *Pine Crossings*. We navigated through rows of homes, each one looking like a replica of the last.

We also found more crazies.

It was just one at first. An older man wearing a dressing gown stumbling down the center of the road. Clara spotted him first, thankfully before he saw us. We ducked into a supermarket parking lot and crouched between the parked cars until he moved on.

A little further down the road we ran into a group of four, a couple and two children, who looked like a family out for a walk on a Sunday afternoon, except that the children wore stained and ripped pajamas and the adults, who we assumed must be their parents, lacked any clothing at all. The woman's pendulous breasts were streaked with what looked like mud, but I had the disconcerting thought that it might be blood. The man had a large gash across his stomach, the edges of the wound turning purple. Again, we ducked out of sight and avoided a confrontation. It was then that I concluded the suburbs were not the best place to be.

"We should find the Interstate," I said, pulling the map from my back pocket.

"Are you sure?" Clara looked worried. "There might be more of them there."

"Probably not as many as there are here." I had given this some thought, and with such a dense population in the subdivisions on the outskirts of the city there were bound to be more crazies ahead. Although we'd been lucky to avoid them so far, I wasn't sure our luck would hold. "Besides, the Interstate will be quicker. We need to get downtown."

"Why downtown?" Darwin asked. "The text message said New Haven. It never said where we should go once we got to New Haven."

"That's true." That thought had occurred to me too, but I also thought it unlikely that the suburbs were the safe zone since we hadn't seen a soul, except for roving crazies, since our arrival. "It would be easier to defend the downtown area than the outlying areas."

"I wish the text messages had been more specific," Clara said. "I thought we would have seen more signs of life by now, military personnel, FEMA, something."

"I agree." Things were too quiet. "But we're here now, so we might as well keep going."

"Well..." Darwin started to protest.

"Unless you have a better place to go?" I cut him off. I was sick of Darwin's attitude today.

"No." He turned away.

"Good." I traced a finger over the map, studying it for a second. "It looks like the Interstate is about a mile east of us. From there it should be a straight run into downtown."

"Let's do it." Clara nodded.

"All right." I got my bearings and folded the map. "We'll see soon enough if New Haven really is a haven."

CHAPTER SEVENTY-FIVE

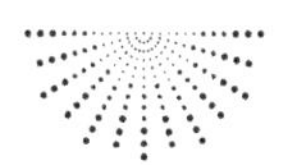

THE INTERSTATE LOOKED VERY MUCH as it did the last time we had traveled it, only here the cars were packed tighter, the wrecks worse. The travel lanes were a mess. In some places burned and smashed vehicles blocked the road entirely, while in others it looked like people had parked where they were and got out.

Mostly we stuck to the shoulder, which was free of cars, and made good time, only stopping twice. Once to duck out of sight when a crazie wandered across the road ahead of us. The second time we stopped was to look at the smashed, burned remains of a small aircraft, a Cessna or similar make, that had taken a nosedive and now lay broken and in pieces. We maneuvered to the left of it, careful to avoid the slick spill of fuel that leaked from a ruptured tank. How it had not exploded was anyone's guess, but it hadn't. We avoided looking into the cockpit, not wanting to see the grisly remains that might be there.

"I hope they died quickly," Clara said.

"I'm sure they did." I wondered if the occupants were even sane when the aircraft went down. There was a chance that they were as nutty as Walter. There was also a chance that they were among the people who had mysteriously disappeared.

It wasn't long after we passed the wrecked plane that we came across the first downtown exit. I stopped and pulled the map out, examining it one last time, and determined that this might be as good a place as any to leave the Interstate behind, even though there was still no sign that New Haven was the safe zone we were promised. Regardless, I didn't want to walk too far and miss whoever had sent me the messages.

"It all looks so normal," Clara said as we walked down the ramp. "The shops, the parked cars." She looked at me. "If it wasn't for the lack of people, the utter stillness of the place, you would think everything was back to normal."

"Not quite," I said. My eyes had picked out a cluster of shapes sprawled on the ground ahead of us, right in the middle of an intersection over which hung several dark, useless traffic lights.

"What is that?" Darwin brought his rifle down. "Are those people?"

"I think so." We were drawing closer now. "And they look like they are dead."

"That's not so strange," Clara said. "We've seen our share of bodies over the last few days."

"Not like this." There was something off with this group. At first I couldn't put my finger on it, but as we approached them it hit me. "They have been shot."

"Oh no. Who would have done that?" Clara looked pale. "Do you think there are more people like Gary here?"

"I hope not." I came to a stop and looked down at the corpses, suddenly realizing that these were not normal people. "Look at their ripped clothes, how dirty they are. These people were infected."

"Crazies?"

"I would put money on it."

"So who shot them?" Clara glanced around. "The place is a ghost town, at least so far."

"An excellent question." I eyed the bullet holes. "Whoever it was, they don't appear to be here now."

"Unless they're keeping out of sight," Darwin said. "Summing us up. Watching us."

"They might be who we're looking for." Clara looked hopeful.

"And they might not be." Just because someone had taken out a bunch of crazies didn't make them friendly. Until yesterday, I would have been overjoyed to see any normal human being. Now I realized we could be in as much danger from the sane humans as the crazy ones.

"We should keep moving." Clara eyed the corpses with a look of revulsion. "I feel like a sitting duck standing here."

"Come on." I stepped away from the dead crazies, dropping my rifle from my shoulder at the same time. "We should be careful from here on in. Someone obviously has some serious firepower, and I don't want to get on the wrong side of them."

"Which way should we go?" Clara asked.

"Beats me." We were at a four-way intersection. One road led back to the Interstate, but the other three stretched off in opposite directions. In the end I picked the route that took us toward the tallest buildings. I pointed. "How about that way?"

"It's as good as anything." Darwin didn't sound convinced, but if he had reservations, he didn't voice them.

When we set off again, he followed a few steps behind, dropping further back occasionally, then hurrying to catch up.

We carried on through downtown, making our way past abandoned storefronts, empty restaurants and tall office towers that sat in silent darkness. The city felt claustrophobic and strange, devoid as it was of the usual beeping horns, screeching tires and hubbub of human interaction. It almost felt like a movie set, something approximating the city, but not quite. When I was a kid, I'd visited Florida. We went to a theme park, and they had a mockup of New York, the fronts of the buildings constructed in forced perspective so that they appeared bigger than they were. A wooden backdrop hovered behind the flat buildings with a skyline painted on it. Fake fire hydrants occupied phony street corners. A yellow cab stood at the curb even though the driver was a dummy, and no passenger would ever climb aboard. The place lacked the soul of a real city, the heartbeat that kept it alive. New Haven felt the same. It didn't feel real. I half believed that if I peeked behind the front façade of one of the buildings now, I would find nothing but a wooden framework and joists holding it up. I felt my disappointment growing with each street we explored.

I was not the only one.

"There's nothing here." Clara came to a stop in the middle of the road. She leaned against a cop car that sat between lanes, the driver's door wide open. Her shoulders sagged. "We're alone."

"We don't know that." It was a feeble attempt to bolster her spirits, especially since I felt the same way, but it was all I had.

"Look around." Tears swelled at the corners of her eyes. "There's nobody. If there ever was anyone here, they are long gone."

"This doesn't make sense." Darwin jumped up on the hood of the police car and lifted his rifle, peering down the barrel as if he was aiming. "Why send those text messages, bring us here, for this?"

"I don't know." I had still harbored hope that my brother was behind the cryptic messages, even though they didn't sound like him. But if the messages were from Jeff, he would never tell me to come here and then leave. Unless something terrible had happened, something that forced whoever had been here to abandon their sanctuary. The problem was, there was no sign of anything other than the usual wrecked cars and crazies. Except for the bullet riddled corpses near the Interstate, and who knew the story behind those?

"I can't go on." Clara sank to the ground, her back against the car. "That's it. I'm done."

"We can't give up." Even if this is not what we were expecting, it doesn't change our predicament. I sat down next to her and took her hand. "What about your family in Florida?"

"I don't even know if they are still alive." She sniffed. "Chances are they are dead or crazy."

"We should try to find out, at least." I didn't like the new Clara, the hopeless one.

"It's a waste of time." She pulled her hand away. "We came all the way here thinking this was some kind of nirvana, our salvation. But it's not. Look at it. It's as messed up as everywhere else. This is it. This is our life from here on out. Scavenging canned goods when we can find them, running from raving lunatics that used to be good, normal people, and living in constant terror that either the huge, nightmarish monsters will eat us, the weather will strike us dead, or we'll wake up crazy. This is no way to live."

Darwin slid down off the car's hood and paced back and forth. "What if we're the last people left?"

"What?" I looked up at him. "That's ridiculous."

"Is it?" He turned to look at me. "Apart from JT and his group and Gary's band of jerks, we haven't run across any other normal people."

"There was Clay." I refused to believe that we were the only people left.

"And for all we know, he went crazy or ended up torn apart by those creatures we saw at the motel," Clara countered. "What are the chances he actually made it to Canada, and that anyone was there to greet him?"

"I don't know." It hurt to admit that things might be worse than I wanted to entertain. After all, Clara was right; there was nobody here. We had fought our way across three states and been through hell just to get to a derelict city. I was about to admit as much when Darwin spoke up, a tremble in his voice.

"Guys, we have to go now."

"Why?" I glanced up.

"Because we aren't as alone as we thought we were."

I followed Darwin's gaze. There, coming along the road, making their way steadily toward us, was a large pack of crazies.

CHAPTER SEVENTY-SIX

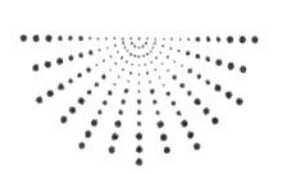

I SPRANG TO MY FEET. There must have been thirty or more crazies in the group, and by the way they were moving I knew they had seen us. I reached down and helped Clara up. "We need to get the hell out of here right now."

"Where did they come from?" Clara asked, her eyes wide with fear.

"Beats me. Can't say I'm surprised, given how we were running into them in the suburbs." I cursed myself for not being more careful.

"At least we have guns now." Darwin was already bringing his weapon to bear, even though the crazies were still a good two hundred feet away.

"Don't." I grabbed him by the arm and dragged him backwards, away from the throng. "Save it for when we need it." I was running now, pulling Darwin and Clara along with me.

"I'm sorry," Clara said as she ran alongside of me.

"What for?"

"Next time I decide to have a breakdown, tell me to wait until we are somewhere safe."

"It's a deal."

"Thanks." She glanced backwards. "Shit. They are gaining on us."

I looked over my shoulder. The crazies were loping along in tight formation, and they were closer than before. Something about the way they moved, tight and in synch, reminded me of a flock of birds. "Damn things are fast."

"We should get off the main drag," Clara said. "Maybe we can find somewhere to hide, get inside somewhere and hole up until they lose interest in us."

"Good idea. How about there?" I pointed toward a service road that sliced between two large buildings, one of which looked like a hotel.

"No good." Clara shook her head. "Look, there's more of them."

From the yawning opening of a parking garage under the hotel, another group of crazies spilled toward us.

"Dammit." Darwin looked out of breath. "How are there so many?"

I ignored him. I was not used to this much running, and already I could feel my breathing becoming labored. When we reached the next four-way intersection, I steered us to the right, down a side street. I had no idea where we were heading, but I wanted to get us out of the crazies' line of sight.

It didn't quite work the way I hoped.

Instead of finding a nice open road ahead of us, we came face to face with another cluster of crazies, and these were much closer. As one, they turned and looked at us, the looks on their faces changing from one of slack jawed indifference to one of hunger.

"Oh, hell." Clara stumbled and came to a stop. "Oh, no."

"Back the other way." I turned, knowing as I did so what I would see.

Rounding the corner, blocking the intersection, came the group we were fleeing from, although their numbers had expanded. I guessed that the crazies from the parking garage had joined them.

"We're trapped." Clara looked like she was going to give up for the second time in as many minutes.

"Then we do the best we can." I looked at Darwin. "You wanted to shoot our way out, well now is the time."

"Finally." He brought his rifle up and took aim, then pulled the trigger. There was a loud bang, and one of the crazies blocking our retreat fell backward. The others barely noticed, and soon he was swallowed up by the crowd. "One down, lots more to go."

"My turn." Clara took aim at the other group of crazies and fired off two rounds in quick succession. Again a crazie went down and lay unmoving on the road. "Like shooting fish in a barrel."

"Don't get too cocky," I warned her as I raised my gun and pulled the trigger. "We have limited ammo, and we don't want to waste it. Shoot to clear a path through."

"Got it." She squeezed off another round, dropping a short bald man wearing a grease stained tee.

"This is a bit like playing a video game." Darwin took down two more.

"Except that you get ripped limb from limb if you miss," I cautioned him while shooting a lone crazie that had broken from the pack and was rushing toward us, arms outstretched.

Clara fired again, then again.

I watched two more crazies take a dive, but still it didn't look as if we had even made a dent in the advancing horde, and at this rate we only had seconds before they would be upon us. "We really need that escape route," I said. "Target the ones on the far right. Maybe we can take out enough of them to skirt around."

"It's no good," Clara said, dropping two more, one after the other, then pulling ammo from her pocket to reload. "Every time I kill one, two more take its place."

"Same here." Darwin was firing in rapid succession. "It's hopeless. There seem to be more of them no matter how many I shoot."

"Just keep firing." The crazies were close now. I braced, expecting to feel their hands tearing at me. Images of the guy back at the school, Emily's friend, being ripped apart, played in my head.

"I'm scared." Clara looked at me. "I don't want to die like this."

"I know." I fired again, blasting a woman in a grocery store uniform just as she was about to grab at me. She swiveled, a shriek of anger escaping her lips. I fired again and this time her head snapped back and she fell to the ground, twitching.

"If you have a plan, now would be a good time to share it." Darwin fumbled to reload.

"If I did, you'd be the first to know!" I said, shouting over the noise of the screeching crazies and the rifle blasts. Only it wasn't just rifle fire I was competing with. There was something else now. From somewhere beyond the milling horde, I recognized the distinctive sound of semi-automatic gunfire.

"Listen." Darwin had heard it too.

"That sounds like machine gun fire." Clara glanced at me. "Oh my God, there's someone else out there."

I was about to reply, but right at that moment there was a popping, whooshing sound, and then the road ahead of us exploded in a bright orange fireball that billowed fifty feet into the air. When it cleared I saw a clear path through the crazies, and I also saw something else.

Soldiers.

CHAPTER SEVENTY-SEVEN

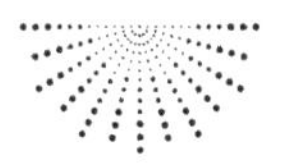

THERE WERE FOUR OF THEM, dressed in heavy black body armor with rigid masks covering their faces. Each soldier carried a mean looking semi-automatic weapon slung over their shoulder. The closest of the four gripped a large tube-like apparatus. This was, I assumed, the instrument that caused the fireball and scattered the crazies, at least those who hadn't been blown apart.

"Come with us." The man with the rocket launcher stepped forward, motioning. "Hurry."

I hesitated for a moment, but then realized that more crazies were bearing down upon us from the other direction. There would be time to find out who these men were later.

I let Clara go first, and then followed, with Darwin at my heel. We hurried past what remained of the first wave of crazies. I avoided looking down, not wanting to see the carnage the rocket-propelled grenade had caused. The crazies were trying to kill us, but only days ago they were normal, everyday folk with jobs and families. To see them lying bloodied and torn apart was not something I took joy in.

Two of the soldiers, including the one with the rocket

launcher, took the lead, while the other two brought up the rear. As we ran, I heard them shooting bursts of automatic fire. Although the explosion had taken out plenty of crazies, there were still many more giving chase.

We turned a corner and found ourselves on another wide street, with two lanes in each direction separated by a narrow grass median. On each side of the road a sidewalk flanked high-end boutiques and restaurants, their windows dark and lifeless. Cars littered the roadway as if they were toys discarded by some giant child. A fire truck sat on its side, blocking two entire lanes. In front of it, sprawled out with arms spread wide, lay the corpse of a firefighter in a bright yellow reflective jacket. His helmet rested next to the curb a few feet away, a dark red slash of something that looked like blood crusted on its crown.

"We have more hostiles ahead," the lead soldier said, his gaze fixed further down the road.

I saw, to my dismay, a band of crazies, one hundred or more, running toward us. The steady clack-clack-clack of gunfire from the soldiers to our rear told me we were still being pursued from that direction, as well.

"There are too many to fight off." The soldier in charge pointed toward a tall Gothic building to our right. "Over there. Head for the building."

"That's not a good idea. We'll be trapped," I said. If the crazies saw us go inside, they would swarm, maybe even surround the building, and then there would be no way out. Worse, if they broke the door down we would be forced to fight them in close quarters.

"We need a defendable position," the soldier snapped back. "Trust me, we will get you out of here in one piece."

"I think we should do as he says." Clara tugged at my arm, glancing down the road toward the approaching swarm of crazies. "We're never going to be able to shoot our way through that many crazies. There are too many."

"Fine." I did not know if these men were friend or foe, but considering the circumstances, I was willing to take my chances.

"Come on." The lead soldier motioned for us to follow him. He hurried across the street to the building and rattled the doors.

They were locked.

He pulled a pistol from his belt, leveled it, and fired once. There was a dull clunk, and then he was pushing the doors inward.

"Much better than a crowbar," Clara said as we stepped across the threshold into a plush tiled lobby with marble columns that ascended two floors high through a central space surrounded by offices. "We're doing that next time we need to break into somewhere."

The last two soldiers entered, pushing the doors closed behind them. A moment later there was a dull thud as the first of the crazies reached the building. I went to the narrow window flanking the door and peered out, dismayed to see more following. Before long a mob of angry crazies pushed against the doors, clamoring to gain entry. Their insane howls sent a shiver up my spine.

"We can't hold them off for long." The soldiers grunted with the effort of holding the doors shut.

"We need something to wedge these doors." The lead soldier looked around, frantic. "Quickly now."

"Try this." Clara pulled the crowbar from her backpack. She stepped forward and slid it between the door handles. "I hope this works."

I watched the doors, my heart racing. If it didn't work, we were dead.

The doors bulged inward.

A pair of fingers wriggled through the gap.

A single eye peered in, looking at us. The crazie uttered a grunt of frustration.

I looked at Clara. She was watching the doors with morbid fascination, biting her lip, no doubt wondering if the crowbar was going to slip and let the crazies come tumbling toward us.

It didn't.

The crowbar was holding. At least for now.

The lead soldier reached up and removed his facemask to reveal a rugged, pitted face with two days of stubble spreading across a square jaw. He turned to me. "Hayden Stone."

"Yes."

"We've been looking for you." His eyes roamed from me to Clara and Darwin. "Who are these people?"

"Friends." I narrowed my eyes, wondering how he knew me. "Now, who exactly are you?"

"Jason Brooks. These guys are Colt, Roberts and Blake." The soldiers nodded as Brooks said their names. "But you already know that, or at least, you did."

"You must have me confused with someone else." I took a step forward, closer to Brooks, bringing my rifle to bear. "I've never met any of you people before."

"Sir?" the soldier identified as Blake spoke up. "We can handle the introductions on the other side. We need to leave."

"Right." Brooks glared at me. "Put that damned rifle down. You don't want to shoot me, I promise you."

I hesitated, and then lowered the weapon.

"That's better." Brooks said. He turned to Blake. "Do we have enough bracelets?"

"Yes, sir." Blake pulled three shiny metal wristbands from his utility belt. He tossed one to me, and the others to Clara and Darwin. "Put these on your right wrist."

I slipped the metal bracelet over my hand and clicked it shut around my wrist. Clara and Darwin followed suit. "What are these?"

"Our way home."

"I don't follow." The bracelet felt cool against my skin. It seemed to vibrate slightly, as if it were pulsing with a low electrical current.

"You will." Brooks said. He turned to the soldier to his left, the man called Colt. "Get us out of here."

"With pleasure." Colt looked at us. "Take a deep breath. And whatever you do, don't breathe back out until we cross over."

"Wait. What does he mean, cross over?" Darwin exclaimed. "Are we really going to trust these people?"

"I don't think we have much choice," I replied. "It's that or get eaten by those crazies out there."

"Do it now!" Brooks barked the command to Colt. The soldier nodded, his fingers dancing across a small touch screen tablet.

The air crackled with an electric hum.

I found myself surrounded by a bright blue halo. Next to me I could see Clara, engulfed in a similar aura of light. My skin tingled as if tiny electric currents were running through it. I took a deep breath and then, as the doors gave way and the first crazies spilled into the lobby, the world shattered around me.

CHAPTER SEVENTY-EIGHT

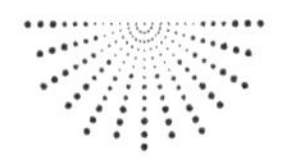

IT FELT LIKE I WAS being pushed through a paper shredder. One minute I was in the building's lobby in New Haven, and the next I was lost in a black void being stretched in every direction at once. I wanted to scream, but I remembered colt's warning not to breathe out. I did not know what would happen if I did, but I didn't want to find out. The pain reached a crescendo. It felt like every atom in my body was being pulled apart. I clenched my hands together, willing the agony to end. And then, just when I thought I was going to die, everything clicked back into place.

I gasped and stumbled forward, a moan escaping my lips. When I composed myself, I realized we were no longer in the lobby of the building in New Haven.

This was a new place.

We were standing on a raised circular grille. A strange blue light pulsed beneath our metallic dais, hypnotic and disturbing at the same time. Several thick wires snaked away to a workstation several feet distant. Behind this sat a man with a pair of round spectacles perched on his nose.

He looked up and watched us for a moment before speaking. "They're back."

"Excellent." A thickset man about fifty years old strode toward us, a wide grin on his face. He approached Brooks. "I was starting to think you had stayed over there."

"Not likely." Brooks stepped from the pad. He turned toward me. "Everyone make it okay?"

My arms and legs tingled, and my heart was racing. "Jesus Christ, what the hell was that?"

"Don't worry, it gets easier the more times you do it," Brooks said.

"Damn, that hurt." Clara was rubbing her arms. "You could have given us some warning."

"Sorry about that." Brooks stretched. "No time."

"Where's Darwin?" Clara looked around, frantic. "He's not here."

"He was right next to me." I searched the group, but did not see him.

"Colt?" Brooks turned to the soldier with the touch screen. "How many people made it through?"

"Hang on, checking now." Colt punched at the screen, a frown furrowing his brow. "Says here that we only transported six. It looks like the seventh bracelet didn't activate."

I took a step forward. "What are you saying?"

"Check again," Brooks said to Colt. "Are you sure?"

"Yes, sir." Colt nodded. "Six activations. One unit didn't power up and make the jump."

"How is that possible?" Clara walked toward Brooks and for a moment I thought she was going to punch him, but she stopped a few feet away and glared. "Are you saying that he's still back there?"

Brooks took a step back. "Yes, unfortunately."

"How?" I felt my anger rising. "You said you were going to get us all out."

"I know," Brooks said. "This happens sometimes. The technology isn't perfect. Do you know how hard it is to punch into another universe?"

"Another universe?" I echoed the words. "What the hell does that mean?"

"You haven't told them?" The thickset man raised an eyebrow.

"No." Brooks shook his head. "We didn't have the time."

Clara walked up to Brooks. "We need to go back right now and get him."

"No, we can't."

"Of course you can. Jump back over, punch through the universe - do whatever you do and go get him! He's in terrible danger. We have to go save him now!"

"Enough." The thickset man raised an arm. "Please, let me explain, and then maybe you will see why we cannot go back and rescue your friend."

"You've got one minute. If you haven't convinced us by then, I'm going back myself," I said. "And no one had better get in my way."

"Fine." The man shook his head. "Please, step this way, both of you. I want to show you something."

I stepped down, looking around as I did so. The room we were in was large, with square concrete pillars dotted at intervals. Apart from the strange equipment, it was sparse. Several people milled about. A few, clearly soldiers just like Brooks, held guns. They seemed on edge.

"My name is Colonel Brand." The stranger introduced himself. "It's been a while. How much do you remember?"

"He doesn't appear to have retained any of his own memories, sir," Brooks interjected.

"My own memories?" I glanced between the two men. "Would someone please tell me what is going on here?"

"Come with me." Brand walked across the room, stopping at a tall window.

I followed, with Clara close behind. I could tell that she was still thinking about Darwin. We both were, but right now there was nothing we could do.

"What do you think?" Brand motioned to the view beyond the window.

A vast metropolis spread out before me, but like no city I had ever seen. Impossibly tall skyscrapers reached high into a dark evening sky, their frames sleek and smooth. Beneath these, far below, lay a network of raised gantries, upon which moved long, thin vehicles that glided with effortless ease. Further down, at ground level, the streets were ablaze with light. From my vantage point, I could make out throngs of people milling around.

"What is this place?" I asked.

"This is your home, Hayden," Brand replied. "Your real home."

"My home is Burlington, Vermont."

"No, it's not." Brand turned to me. He gripped my arm. "That place, that world, it's not what you think."

"I don't understand."

"I know you don't." Brand sighed. "What would you say if I told you that the world you just came from, the place that you thought was your home, is in reality, an artificially constructed parallel world?"

"I'd say you are crazy."

"Yes. No doubt. But what I speak is the truth." Brand gazed out over the city. "They took you from us. Your memory was wiped, and they placed you in that world as an example."

"An example of what?"

"The honesty of our government," Brand said. "After all, if you, the leader of the *One World* movement, were to change your tune, go and live on a parallel world, it would validate their agenda, and fracture the opposition."

"One World?" I looked at him, confused.

"Yes," Brand said. "Twenty years ago our government sent people into parallel dimensions. Worlds created by scientists solely to relieve the pressures of overpopulation here on Earth. Unfortunately, the worlds are not stable, a fact the government does its best to keep hidden. For the last six years we have been pushing back, telling people the truth."

"One World." I nodded. "You're a resistance group."

"A crude way to put it, but yes. And you are our founder."

"Me?"

"Yes." Brand nodded. "They caught you raiding a government facility, attempting to steal documents that would prove all of our claims. They did things to you, broke you, and tortured you."

"I don't remember any of this."

"Of course you don't. They made you denounce One World, then they wiped your memories and dumped you in that decaying universe to die."

"The crazies, the disappearing people, the strange creatures."

"Byproducts of a failing world. One reality is merging with another, collapsing in. Sometimes things get dragged over from one reality to the other. Sometimes people go the other way, or worse, get trapped between the two and go crazy. This is nothing we haven't seen before. Eventually the world will reach a point where it can't sustain itself at all, and then-"

"What?"

"And then it will cease to exist, dragging any other dimensions it has collapsed into along with it."

Clara looked out over the city, an expression of awe on her face. Brooks hovered a few feet behind, his own expression bland and emotionless.

"So we were all living a lie?" Clara addressed Brand. There was a faint note of sadness in her voice.

"Yes." Brand met her gaze. "I'm sorry."

"And Darwin is still there, in that collapsing universe."

"I'm afraid so." Brooks spoke up, looking uncomfortable.

"So what are we waiting for?" Clara glanced down at the bracelet on her wrist. "Let's go back and get him."

"I agree with Clara," I said. "I've given you your minute, now it's time to get our friend back."

"The problem is, that's not possible." Brand shook his head. "If we try to jump back into the other universe right now, we will be torn to pieces. We can only cross over and back to the same worlds once in any twenty-four-hour period. We're literally ripping a hole in the fabric of space-time and it needs time to repair itself. Think of it like throwing a rock into a pond, and the ripples it causes. If you throw another rock right away, the ripples get worse, but if you wait a while, the ripples from the first rock fade away. If we jump again right now, all we'll be doing is killing ourselves. It would be suicide, trust me."

"So send someone else," I said.

"It doesn't matter who we send. It's not the person, it's the act of punching through."

"You could at least try. You can't know for sure that it would cause a problem."

"But we do. We lost five men several months ago making a second jump too soon." Brooks looked apologetic. I wondered if it was just for show. "I know it's not what you want to hear, but it is the reality of the situation."

"We can't just leave him there to die," Clara protested.

"And we can't go back to get him." Brooks was adamant.

"So that's it?" A tear formed in Clara's eye. "We just abandon him?"

"Even if we could go back, he's probably already dead. The

doors gave way just as we jumped. You saw it. The place must have been overrun in seconds."

"We don't know that he's dead." The anguish on her face was heartbreaking. I knew how she felt. It was bad enough losing Emily, but to lose Darwin right when we were on the cusp of safety seemed especially cruel.

"I'm sorry." Brooks turned away. "There's nothing I can do."

"Bullshit." Clara whirled around and pushed past him, fleeing, with tears streaming down her face.

I watched her go, a feeling of helplessness roiling in my gut. I opened my mouth to call after her, to comfort her, but I didn't, because deep down, I knew there was nothing I could say that would make a bit of difference.

CHAPTER SEVENTY-NINE

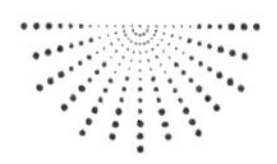

IT WAS LATE.

I sat on a cot in a small room off the main area. Brand provided the accommodations. He insisted we get some sleep, even though sleeping was the last thing on my mind.

Opposite me, on an identical cot, Clara sat with her head in her hands. She had not spoken since the confrontation with Brooks, but now she raised her head and looked at me. "Do you think he's still alive?"

"I don't know."

"It's so unfair, just leaving him there like that."

"Yes, it is," I agreed. "But what could we have done?"

"We should have gone back."

"You heard Brooks." I reached out and took her hand. Her skin felt soft and warm. "It wouldn't have worked. Whatever technology they use to move between dimensions must have its limitations."

"You believe him?" Clara asked. "You believe everything they have told you since we got here?"

"I don't see any reason not to."

"I don't trust them."

"Me either." It would take more than a few well-placed words, a fanciful story, to convince me we were among friends. I had spent the last hour wracking my brain, trying to remember anything of what Brand had told me, but it was no use. For now, I would have to take their word for it that I was their erstwhile leader, insane as the whole thing sounded.

"I want to go back for him." Clara wiped a tear from her eye. "I want to see for myself."

"I was thinking the same thing." I shifted my position, moving over to her cot, sitting down next to her. "Tomorrow I'll tell Brooks that we have to go back."

"You think he'll agree?"

"I don't see that he has any choice," I said. "Amnesia or not, they claim I'm their leader. That has to be worth something."

"Thank you." She rested her head on my shoulder.

"For what?"

"Looking out for me. Being there." She paused. "For understanding."

"You're welcome." I stroked her hair. "I won't let anything happen to you."

"I know." She looked up into my face and smiled through the tears.

I returned her gaze, my eyes finding hers. For a while we stayed like that, sharing an unspoken understanding.

I brushed a tear from her cheek.

She leaned close, her eyes expectant and wide.

And then I kissed her, my lips finding hers in a long, lingering embrace. She slipped her arms around me and held me close. I had no idea what the future may hold, or even who I really was, but I knew one thing.

We were together.

And in that moment, as we held each other tight, it was all we had, and it was enough. It had to be.

THE END

Made in the USA
Las Vegas, NV
09 January 2023

65255036R00164